Paul Mendes-Flohr

Professor of Philosophy,
Hebrew University, Jerusalem,
Editor, Contemporary Jewish Religious Thought

re: Summa 1

"...there is no comparable volume offering such a comprehensive,
authoritative and intelligible discussion of the problem... a remarkable
effort to offer a fresh approach."

Louis Dupré

Professor of Religious Studies, Yale University

re: Summa 1

"...an original, and, in this reader's opinion, a very promising point of
view...the author gathers a philosophically coherent and, in the end,
highly modern insight... a unified metaphysics..."

Joseph Dan

Professor of Kabbalah, Hebrew University,
Jerusalem

re: Summa 1

"A major work...a great intellectual and spiritual effort"

Lawrence H. Schiffman

Professor of Hebrew and Judaic Studies
New York University

re: Summa 1 & 2

"It is early for me to say with certainty,
but I am inclined to think that Summa Metaphysica
represents the dawn of the period of metaphysical revision."

Deepak Chopra

Thought Leader in Metaphysics

re: Summa 1, 2 & 3

re: Potentialism Theory

"I'm totally on board with David Birnbaum" - Oct, 2018

see 1-on-1 focus-video Chopra1000.com

21st CENTURY PUBLISHING
150+ AUTHORS/SCHOLARS

www.SummaMetaphysica.com

www.David1000.com

David.Birnbaum.NY@gmail.com

Summa
Metaphysica Ⅳ

**Revised Edition
December 2021**

www.Summa-4.com

online flip-book

POTENTIAL drives the universe - **Birnbaum**

Potentialism Theory

Q4P[∞]

·COSMIC· COSMIC WOMB OF POTENTIAL PARADIGM·

BOOK 4

Summa
Metaphysica IV

QUANTUM MAN

quantum-potential

D A V I D   B I R N B A U M

M ORPHED
COSMIC
ORDER

INFINITE QUEST FOR POTENTIAL[∞]
→ COMPLEXIFICATION
→ EXTRAORDINARIATION

Advanced Summa

Suis Generis Code?

Is $Q4P^\infty$ actually a self-generating, self-building-out,
universe-spanning, quasi-alive, self-sustaining, all-embracing,
all-pervading, pinnacle natural force, quasi- computer-code -

ongoing executing/building-out
the Birnbaum *Super-Formula*

$Q4P^\infty \rightarrow C+ \rightarrow E+$

- from the Get-Go ?

see **Super-Formula1000.com**

3 EPOCHS:

THE 3 EPOCHS TO-DATE OF OUR UNIVERSE

[3 EPOCHS, 2 BIRTHS]

I	**Pure Potential**
II	**Infinite Quest for Potential$^\infty$**
III	**Potential / Reality HYBRID**

see **Chronology1000.com**

Summa Metaphysica series
Summa I - *Religious Man: God and Evil* (1988)
Summa II - *Spiritual Man: God and Good* (2005)
Summa III - *Secular Man: The Transcendent Dynamic* (2014)
Summa IV - *Quantum Man: Morphed Cosmic Order* (2020)

ISBN 978-0-9801710-5-1
53300>

9 780980 171051

'everywhere in nature'

"Algorithms and computation take place not just in computers or between computer systems but actually everywhere in nature, in atoms, in matter,.... bacteria in a cell, and neurons in the brain."

- Avi Wigderson (Israeli mathematician)
  ABEL Prize Co-Winner 3/2021
  Princeton Institute for Advanced Study
  upon learning of hs winning the ABEL Award

David Birnbaum is a graduate of CCNY Engineering
[with a major in Computer Science]
and of Harvard University

He has served on the faculty of the New School (for Social Research) in NY

metaphysics: Summa I (1988); Summa II (2005); Summa III (2014); Summa IV (2020)

Summa Metaphysica series
1988, 2005, 2014, 2020

a universal & unified & fully-integrated

philosophy / metaphysics / cosmology / teleology

"No flaw has been discerned" - Huffington Post 6/10/15
HuffPost1000.com

SummaMetaphysica.com

DAVID BIRNBAUM
SUMMA METAPHYSICA :
A PHILOSOPHY/COSMOLOGY SERIES

Q4P$^\infty$

• *a hitherto undiscerned overarching dynamic*

David Birnbaum Summa Metaphysica philosophy treatise proposes its signature Potentialism Theory.

"Potentialism proposes that there is, indeed, a protagonist to the cosmic order, but that the protagonist is a 'quest', and not a 'classic entity'. The universe quests for its maximal potential. The core dynamic Quest for Potential (Q4P∞) strives with purpose and direction towards ever-greater and higher potential. At the 'beginning of time', eternal Quest for Potential (Q4P∞) harnessed the eternal equations of Physics-Mathematics to ignite our universe via the Big Bang. This same symbiotic dynamic - Quest for Potential (Q4P∞) in league with Physics-Math - then acted as a catalyst for life, evolution, language, emotion, consciousness, and, indeed, for all the key dynamics which have evolved in the universe."

"POTENTIAL DRIVES THE UNIVERSE" - BIRNBAUM

our 'Smart Universe' driven by our hypothesized *natural force* (Q4P)

see also

www.CoreBuildingBlocks.com

"NO FLAW HAS BEEN DISCERNED"

"What drives our universe? The great Greek philosophers were ultimately stymied, as is contemporary physics. A contemporary 21st century independent scholar and metaphysicist, **David Birnbaum** of Manhattan, proposes that 'Potential' drives the universe.

He hypothesizes the core cosmic dynamic to be what he labels Infinite Quest for Potential. Over 150 articles and reviews in dozens of journals (see SummaCoverage.com) have dissected and analyzed the compelling and fully-integrated theory over the course of a quarter century; no flaw has been discerned."

> – Huffington Post
> June 10, 2015
> [see CracksCosmicCode.com]

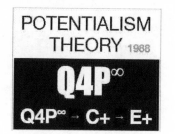

SummaCoverage.com

Summa Metaphysica series

POTENTIALISM THEORY

BOOK SPINES

Summa Metaphysica I — GOD AND EVIL — BIRNBAUM — New Paradigm / Harvard Matrix — 1988

Summa Metaphysica II — GOD AND GOOD — BIRNBAUM — New Paradigm / Harvard Matrix — 2005

Summa Metaphysica III — THE TRANSCENDENT DYNAMIC — BIRNBAUM — New Paradigm / Harvard Matrix — 2014

Summa Metaphysica IV — MORPHED COSMICORDER — BIRNBAUM — New Paradigm / Harvard Matrix — 2020

Summa Metaphysica — ARTICLES ON SUMMA — BIRNBAUM — New Paradigm / Harvard Matrix

a fully integrated & unified -

metaphysics / cosmology / philosophy / teleology / theodicy

Summa 1-4 are available online and, via Amazon,
in Softcover & Kindle.

[Q4P" is Birnbaum's signature Quest for Potential" cosmology theory
first presented in embryonic form in Summa I (1988)]

Summa Metaphysica I
Religious Man:
God and Evil
focus: *theodicy & eternal origins*
(1988)
Summa-1.com

Summa Metaphysica II
Spiritual Man:
God and Good
focus: *metaphysics & teleology*
(2005)
Summa-2.com

Summa Metaphysica III
Secular Man:
The Transcendent Dynamic
focus: *cosmology & evolution*
(2014)
Summa-3.com

Summa Metaphysica IV
Quantum Man:
Morphed Cosmic Order
focus: *quantum-potential*
(2020)
Summa-4.com

Supplement
Summa Metaphysica:
Articles on Summa
(articles from 2013 and onward)
[book is on SummaMetaphysica.com only]
Summa-supplement.com

remember

C+
Complexification

is radically richer & fuller than just -
increasingly-more-of-the-same

see Complexification1000.com

a universal & unified & fully-integrated

POTENTIALISM THEORY

philosophy / metaphysics / cosmology / teleology

a universal metaphysics
POTENTIALISM THEORY
carving-out space for spirituality

Summa Metaphysica

Course Text

Summa Metaphysica by David Birnbaum

Course Text
Summa I and/or Summa II and/or Summa III

University of California
Los Angeles, CA (UCLA)

Gresham College
London, United Kingdom

Brandeis University
Waltham, Massachusetts

Hebrew University
Jerusalem, Israel

Yeshiva University
New York, New York

Union Theological Seminary
New York, New York

Hartford Seminary
Hartford, Connecticut

Jewish Theological Seminary
New York, New York

Emory University
Atlanta, Georgia

Regis University
Denver, Colorado

Stetson University
Deland, Florida

Harding University
Memphis, Tennessee

Gratz College
Melrose Park, Pennsylvania

University of Wales
Cardiff, United Kingdom

University of Windsor
Ontario, Canada

Graduate Theological Union
Berkeley, California

David Birnbaum

note: The logo representation is, of course, not an institutional endorsement of the
Summa Metaphysica philosophical paradigm by the respective colleges/seminaries

see **SummaCoverage.com**

journals coverage

Journals which have featured Summa Metaphysica

NEWSVINE
New Paradigm Designer

MANHATTAN JEWISH SENTINEL
the Riddle of God and Evil

UNIVERSITIES NEWS
Paradigm Wars

CNN IREPORT
100 Elements + Potentialism
= Humanity

IDEAS TAP
An Imaginary 2014 Discussion:
Aristotle and David Birnbaum

DIGITAL JOURNAL
A scientific view of the God question

AUSTRALIAN TIMES
Potentialism v.
Randomness/Atheism

**THEOLOGICAL STUDIES
GEORGETOWN UNIVERSITY**
A Solution to Theodicy

ACADEMIA.EDU
Fractals: The Mathematical
Underpinnings of Potentialism

frontiers

FRONTIERS IN SCIENCE
Potentialism or
String Theory?

YAHOO! VOICES
Intellectual Pursuit Versus
Collegiate Orthodoxy

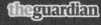

THE GUARDIAN
Has David Birnbaum solved
the mystery of existence

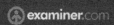

EXAMINER
Summa Metaphysica –
Philosophy, Is there a Purpose?

**JSTOR: INTERNATIONAL JOURNAL
FOR PHILOSOPHY & RELIGION**
A Jewish Perspective

AAR AMERICAN ACADEMY *of* RELIGION

**JOURNAL OF THE AMERICAN
ACADEMY OF RELIGION**
The Problem of Evil

EPOCH TIMES

EPOCH TIMES
Iconoclast Birnbaum:
The Eastern Influence

THE SOUTH AFRICAN
The Colonies Revolt: II

Logical Science
World's leading source for Science and Technology

LOGICAL SCIENCE
Q4P: What Is It? Why Do We Care?

INDEPENDENT SANTA BARBARA
Global Battle over Metaphysics

HERITAGE JOURNAL
An Original Metaphysics

THE HUFFINGTON POST
Two Schemas of the Universe

LONG ISLAND JEWISH WORLD
Cracking the Cosmic Code

THE CANADIAN CATHOLIC REVIEW
God and Evil, A Jewish Perspective

JEWISH WORLD REVIEW
A Unified Theodicy/Theology/Philosophy

THE EXPOSITORY TIMES
The Birnbaum Theodicy

FUTURE TECH
7000 Years in the Making

THE JEWISH REVIEW
Birnbaum's God and Evil

JUDAICA BOOK NEWS
An Original Theodicy

SCIENCERAY
Does The Universe Self-iterate?

JEWISH TRIBUNE
The Birnbaum Theodicy

BROOWAHA
Transcendent Force?

OLSHIN EDUCATION PROGRAM
God and Good

AMAZON.COM
God and Evil

FIRST THINGS
God and Evil

PARIS MATCH
Wiesel & Birnbaum

WORLD.EDU
21st Century paradigm challenge

LERA BLOG
Checkmate

NEWZEALAND TIMES
Cosmic Gateway

BEFORE IT'S NEWS
Defining the Universe?

SETI HOME (Berkeley)
The Pattern to Cosmic Advance

BERKELEY
The Pattern to Cosmic Advance

REGENT COLLEGE (COSMOS)
Physicist Tegmark v. Metaphysicist Birnbaum

BIOLOGICAL SCIENCES (UNT)
Three Views on Evolution

RPI
How to Crack the Cosmic Code

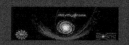

MILKYWAY @ HOME (BERKELEY & RPI)
How to Crack the Cosmic Code

MAX-PLANCK
Unifying Aristotle and Einstein

MILWAUKEE
Unifying Aristotle and Einstein

EINSTEIN @ HOME / MAX PLANCK INST
Unifying Aristotle and Einstein

LIFERAY
The Cosmic T-Shirt

UC RIVERSIDE
The Universal Computer and the Cosmic Womb

QCN (STANFORD / UC RIVERSIDE)
The Universal Computer and the Cosmic Womb

STANFORD
The Universal Computer and the Cosmic Womb

ASH CENTER (HARVARD KENNEDY)
The Theory of Potential & MIT's Finest

COLUMBIA UNIVERSITY
Potentialism for Teens

POCKET KNOWLEDGE
Potentialism for Teens

UNIVERSITY OF NORTH TEXAS
Galapagos: Evolution: the revolutionary hypothesis...

JUBILEE NEWSPAPER
Is God Dead? Hawking v. Birnbaum

see **Summa-Supplement.com**

published by NEW PARADIGM MATRIX

Summa Metaphysica IV - Quantum Man - Morphed Cosmic Order

Q4P Theory

Summa Theory

Potentialism Theory

Birnbaum Theory

Quantum Man Theory

*

Revised Edition October 2020

Library of Congress Cataloging-in-Publication Data

Birnbaum, David.

Morphed Cosmic Order / David Birnbaum.

ISBN 978-0-9801710-5-1

1. Metaphysics.   2. Morphed Cosmic Order.   I. Title.

www.NewParadigmMatrix.com

Direct contact to Editor-in-Chief

David.Birnbaum.NY@gmail.com

POTENTIALISM
THEORY 1988

Q4P$^\infty$

Q4P$^\infty$ → **C+** → **E+**

SUMMA METAPHYSICA

see also

www.SalientMedia.com

Classic Issues Aligned

POTENTIALISM THEORY

THE SUMMA METAPHYSICA SERIES

a unified
(consistent, overarching, fully integrated)
conceptual line of attack

metaphysics
cosmology
philosophy

aligning

eternal origins
Life Force
direction/teleology/driver
purpose/meaning
evolutionary theory
universe horizon

via
**one Common Denominator
dynamic***

- with **theogony** and **theodicy** *in the mix from* a
Religious perspective, and, *loosely defined,* still
in the mix from a Spiritual or Secular perspective

* Q4P ⟶ C+ ⟶ E+

[reprinted from Summa II]

per Summa,

Infinite Quest for Potential
(Q4P)
is a ubiquitous and overarching cosmic dynamic...

Quest for the fulfillment/actualization of this dynamic
is the underlying core drive
of the *cosmic order*...

All of the countless components of the universe,
including humans,
are striving towards the full realization
of their particular potentialities....

- Professor Andrei Alyokhin*

*see UnifyingConcept.com

Q4P[∞]

Quest for Potential
(infinitely recursive)

Q4P (Q4P (Q4P ...

Quest for Potential

within

Quest for Potential

within

Quest for Potential

ad infinitum

Overview of Summa Series

core theme (spanning all 4 works):

Potential drives the universe

1988 (Summa I) Religious Man

theodicy / theology / intellectuality

Proposed Theodicy/Theogony resolution/finesse
closes two key and salient philosophical vulnerabilities in Religion

the 'Unified Formulation'

The God of Potential

'Tree of No Risk' v. 'Tree' of Potential'

Proposed theory centerpiece - pinnacle dynamic Infinite Quest for Potential -
overthrows all classic metaphysics,
and lays the groundwork for Directional Universe

Q4P$^\infty$ is a *natural* albeit pinnacle dynamic;
not a *supernatural* pinnacle dynamic

2005 (Summa II) Spiritual Man

An overarching (powerful and original) metaphysics/cosmology

Cosmic Tool Kit

Demonstrates Directional Universe

Proposed formula cracks the cosmic code

The cosmos is most certainly directional, and most certainly not random

Provides an Overarching Metaphysics / Simultaneous Solution

Provides new metaphysical/ cosmological/philosophical '*standing*' to
Spirituality

The Birnbaum SuperFormula
$Q4P \to C+ \to E+$
provides a formula for the Cosmic Order [an original Teleology]

2014 (Summa III)   Secular Man

'Potentialism Evolution' theory – with MIT in the mix.
  [displaces Random Mutation / Natural Selection]

A universal, unified, seamless & fully-integrated metaphysics/cosmology

Overthrows *Randomness* across multiple fronts
  (including vis à vis Cosmology and Evolution)

MIT's Quantum Mechanics Professor Seth Lloyd
  reinforces our theory with his book *Programming the Universe* (2006)

Creation Ex [infinite] Potential

intro to Chronology of the Universe

2020 (Summa IV)   Quantum Man

What *reality* is our universe?

The Organic Proactive Supercomputer Super-Organism

Starship Universe

Morphed universe at Big Bang point
    from 100% Metaphysical > Physical-Metaphysical hybrid

Morphed Q4P at Big Bang point

'*Connected-at-the-hip*': Q4P- Quantum Mechanics

The universe: *Not your ordinary Life Form*

Q4P$^\infty$: The true universal, pinnacle natural force Driver of Evolution;
    the Driver of '*Birnbaumian Evolution*'

Q4P$^\infty$: the Cosmic Instinct (among other things)

Suis Generis Code/Coding

Three Epochs of our universe

Chronology of the Cosmos: Eternal Origins > today

'Second Law'

Potentialism

a unified & fully integrated - theory / hypothesis

"*quod erat demonstrandum*"

- D. Birnbaum / NY

"1960"

1960
Age 10
Forest Hills, Queens, NY

Modern Orthodox Jewish American

The sparkling new Jewish Day School buildings had been going up

The science labs and science teachers were pretty good, as well

[Evolution was treated as fact.
Darwinism was taught as the prevailing theory to that effect.]

America was on the ascent

[JFK elected Nov 1960]

Life was not bad

Post-Holocaust

[the Death Camps has been liberated in 1945 by US GIs and the
Russians; 2/3 of European Jewery had been murdered]

The uber-trauma was 99% invisible in Forest Hills - but was there

#A Where had the God of Israel been? Was there, indeed, a Prime
Mover? If yes, what is the true nature of this Prime Mover?

No answers.

The family bible is/was inscribed -

by my father's father -

"Avenge the murder of my father 1944"
(meaning, my great-grandfather)
Rabbi David Birnbaum
Czechoslovakia
1944

Post Big Bang Theory

(Proposed 1927; partially confirmed 1964
at Bell Labs, New Jersey)

#B But what had instigated the Big Bang? Was there
a direction/goal to the universe?

And what - if anything - had transpired in the time
between Eternal Origins and the Big Bang?

No answers.

But, wait
might questions
#A and #B
have essentially the same *core* answer?

2020
Age 70
Rockefeller Center
Manhattan

Summa IV published

#C Yes / ***Simultaneous*** *Path to Resolution*

See 4-volume SummaMetaphysica.com,
but this Summa 4 alone
covers the science bases -
and alludes to the spiritual/ theological -
dealt-with more fully in Summa 1 & 2

Some projects take longer than others…

thank you for your gracious patience

*

[4 grandchildren & counting]
2 in the Greater NY area + 2 in Jerusalem

We hope we have been true
to the mandate of
10-yr-old David Birnbaum

We hope we have requited
his *will* and *intuitive confidence*

*

David Birnbaum Bio

David Birnbaum is a philosophical writer, conceptual theorist, historical chronicler and editor.

universal secular philosophy & Jewish religious philosophy:

Birnbaum is known globally as "the architect of Potentialism Theory" – a unified philosophy/cosmology/metaphysics. The paradigm-challenging theory - presented through three prisms - is delineated in Birnbaum's 4-volume Summa Metaphysica series (1988, 2005, 2014, 2020). See Summa1000.com.

A riposte to Summa Theologica of (St.) Thomas Aquinas, the (original) Birnbaum treatise challenges both the mainstream Western philosophy of Aristotelianism as well as the well propped-up British/atheistic cosmology of Randomness.

The Summa Metaphysica series was the focus of an international academic conference on Science & Religion April 16-19, 2012 at BARD College (see Conference1000.com).

The focus of over 150 reviews and articles, Summa Metaphysica has been an assigned Course Text at over 15 institutions of higher learning globally. The work has been very widely covered globally. (see SummaCoverage.com for 100+ articles on the series as well as the Course Text institutions.

The first volume of the Summa series, God and Evil (KTAV, 1988) is considered by many to be a breakthrough modern day classic in the field of religious philosophy and of theodicy, in particular. See also GodOfPotential.com

Signature metaphysical themes:

Cosmic Womb of Potential
The God of Potential
Quest for Potential∞
Q4P∞ → C+ → E+
Complexification (C+)
Extraordinariation (E+)

Super-Formula
Suis Generis Code/Coding
Three Epochs
Chronology1000

editor, Jewish thought & spirituality:

David Birnbaum is the conceptualizer and Editor-in-Chief of the Mesorah Matrix series on Jewish thought and spirituality. The series spans 10-volumes with 10 respective themes and includes 200+ original pieces from 150+ global Jewish thought leader essayists. See Mesorah1000.com.

historical chronicler and author:

In the history realm, David Birnbaum is the author/chronicler of the 2-volume The Crucifixion – of the Jews. The 2-volume set (published in 2009) traces a direct trajectory from the Canon Gospels in the First Century to Auschwitz in the Twentieth. In November 2019, ten years after the publication of The Crucifixion, the Church of England / Anglican Communion issued a major document/report "God's Unfailing Word" - which accepted/confirmed many of the key thrusts of the (highly-controversial) Birnbaum frontal challenge to the Church of a decade prior.
See Crucifixion1000.com.

The inter-related Birnbam history series is his 7-volume Jews, Church and Civilization. See Civilization1000.com.

education:

He is a graduate of Yeshiva of Forest Hills (Dov Revel), Yeshiva University High School (MTA), City College of New York (CCNY), and Harvard (1974).

[David B's BSc degree is in Computer Science from CCNY's Engineering School;
the major contained within its fold both System Simulation and Formal Logic focuses - aside from sundry data science and programming courses.]

faculty:

New School for Social Research (1983)
[*aka* The New School]
New York, NY

See also NewParadigmCatalyst.com, David1000.com

DAVID BIRNBAUM MAJOR WORKS

As Author

4-volume Summa Metaphysica (www.philosophy1000.com)

2-volume The Crucifixion (www.crucifixion1000.com)

7-volume Jews, Church & Civilization (www.civilization1000.com)

As Editor-in-Chief

10-volume Mesorah Matrix (www.mesorah1000.com)
[Jewish Thought & Spirituality ... 150+ authors]

As Conceptualizer

3-volume Summa Spinoffs (www.Spinoffs1000.com)

8-volume Potentialism Theory via Graphic-Narrative
(www.TheoryGraphics1000.com)

As Commentator

www.ManhattanObserver.com

YouTube channels

Summa Metaphysica

Mesorah Matrix

DAVID BIRNBAUM MAJOR WORKS

Summa Metaphysica series

presenting new paradigm
Potentialism Theory
a universal, unified, seamless & fully-integrated
overarching philosophy

www.SummaMetaphysica.com

Summa I:
Religious Man: God and Evil: focus: ***theodicy & eternal origins*** [1988]**

Summa II:
Spiritual Man: God and Good: focus: ***metaphysics & teleology*** [2005]

Summa III:
Secular Man: The Transcendent Dynamic: focus: ***cosmology & evolution*** [2014]

Summa IV:
Quantum Man: Morphed Cosmic Order: focus: ***quantum-potential*** [2020]

see also secondary site PotentialismTheory.com

see also: RewindSumma.com 222+ panel Scroll-Down tour

YouTube Channel: Summa Metaphysica

see also Supplement: Articles on Summa
(only online - on www.SummaMetaphysica.com)

** see also: www.GodOfPotential.com
** see special YouTube channel: www.UnifyingScienceSpirituality.com

SUMMA SPINOFFS

www.Spinoffs1000.com

Cosmic Womb of Potential

God's 120 Guardian Angels

The Lost Manual

TABLE OF CONTENTS

Summa
Metaphysica IV
D A V I D   B I R N B A U M

Morphed Cosmic Order
TABLE OF CONTENTS

cont'd

Summa
MetaphysicaIV
DAVID BIRNBAUM

Morphed Cosmic Order
TABLE OF CONTENTS

cont'd

Summa
Metaphysica IV
DAVID BIRNBAUM

Morphed Cosmic Order
TABLE OF CONTENTS

MORPHED COSMIC ORDER

21st CENTURY PUBLISHING
150+ AUTHORS/SCHOLARS

www.RewindSumma.com

Section A

MORPHED COSMIC ORDER

* BULLETPROOF *

POTENTIALISM THEORY

"NO FLAW HAS BEEN DISCERNED"

A first-hand inspection of Galapagos Island
(of Darwinian fame)

POTENTIALISM THEORY

unequivocally supports Potentialism
over Darwinism

"A COMPELLING HYPOTHESIS"

POTENTIALISM THEORY

AN ORIGINAL & CUTTING-EDGE METAPHYSICS

21st CENTURY GAME CHANGER

POTENTIALISM THEORY

UNIFYING SCIENCE & SPIRITUALITY

A universe replete with potential & possibility

POTENTIALISM THEORY

beckons-forth

MORPHED COSMIC ORDER

Potentialism Theory = Summa Theory = Birnbaum Theory

= Q4P Theory = Quantum Man Theory

= Three Epochs Theory = Cosmic Womb of Potential Theory

David Birnbaum

POTENTIAL DRIVES THE UNIVERSE

QuantumMan.net   ISBN # 978-0-578-68516-8   subtitle: 'ultimate journey'   222+ panels
(c) 2020 by David Birnbaum NY faculty affiliation: New School for Social Research

דוד אריה בן אברהם יעקב הלוי

Core Issues

classic hitherto key unresolved core issues in
metaphysics / cosmology / philosophy / biology:

What *ignited* our universe?

What *drives* our universe?

Is there a *direction* to our universe?

What *really drives* evolution?

Is there one succinct simultaneous answer to all of the above? Yes.

There is only one dynamic which is truly eternal -

Potential

Thus, I crafted a cosmology with that eternal dynamic - Potential -

as the 'spinal column' - or the core -

threading through every stage of the metaphysics.

The core proposition -

The core proposition
is that there is a
single, overarching, and quasi-eternal
dynamic
hitherto undiscerned

Quest for Potential$^\infty$
aka Q4P

which drives the Cosmic Order

"Sorry for the inconvenience, but this is a revolution"

– Subcomandante Marcos
Leader, EZLN
Mayan farmers' revolutionary movement
Chiapas, Mexico, 1994

Potentialism Theory = Summa Theory = Birnbaum Theory = Q4P Theory = Quantum Man Theory

'What Breathes Fire into the Equations?'

for direct link to Huffington Post online archive,

www.CracksCosmicCode.com

David Birnbaum Cracks the Cosmic Code

06/10/2015 6:09 pm

What Breathes Fire into the Equations?

How 21st century Quest for Potential Theory elegantly cracks the cosmic code

David Birnbaum answers Stephen Hawking

What drives our universe? The great Greek philosophers were ultimately stymied, as is contemporary physics. A contemporary 21st century independent scholar and metaphysicist, David Birnbaum of Manhattan, proposes that 'Potential' drives the universe.

Independent scholar and metaphysicist, David Birnbaum.

He hypothesizes the core cosmic dynamic to be what he labels Infinite Quest for Potential. Over 150 articles and reviews in dozens of journals (see SummaCoverage.com) have dissected and analyzed the compelling and fully-integrated theory over the course of a quarter century; no flaw has been discerned.

In discussing Infinite Quest for Potential (shorthand: Q4P), we will look at some crucial gaps in 20th century physics and philosophy. Our literary vehicle will be through a hypothetical give-and-take between two important philosophical thought leaders: Physicist Stephen Hawking of Cambridge and Metaphysicist David Birnbaum of Manhattan.

Hawking's work *The Grand Design* (2010) actually negates any possibility of a 'grand design'; Birnbaum is the author of the 3-part *Summa Metaphysica* series (1988, 2005, 2014) and its associated Potentialism Theory which ascribes 'grand design' to our universe via his hypothesized metaphysical dynamic Infinite Quest for Potential.

Renowned contemporary British physicist Stephen Hawking has given us a number of memorable one-liners regarding physics and the universe. And when Hawking speaks, people do listen. He is a 'pinnacle player' and one of the leading minds in physics. Hawking has given a lot of conjecture over the years -- snippets of hope and tidbits of wisdom for universal understanding; however, the great Hawking, like his erstwhile contemporaries in academe, ultimately leaves key questions unanswered.

Many believe that David Birnbaum's unified Potentialism Theory elegantly lances the key (historical and hitherto intractable) issues in metaphysics via his proposed core dynamic Infinite Quest for Potential -- proposed as the cosmic constant (albeit a quite vibrant constant). Let's see if the Birnbaum theory has the capability to adequately address the great Hawking's questions. First, we need to understand a few concepts from Summa Metaphysica.

Summa Metaphysica's Potentialism Theory

Per Birnbaum, there is an overarching natural cosmic dynamic which Birnbaum hypothesizes as being Infinite Quest for Potential. According to Birnbaum, this one dynamic is eternal and infinitely iterating; it ignited our universe; it drives our universe forward to this very day; it instigated and sustains life; its goal is to seek-after maximal/optimal Potential.... inexorably. In other words, if it exists it is the ultimate 'silver bullet' for metaphysics.

As per the *Summa Metaphysica* website:

"Infinite Quest for Potential (infinitely iterating) is the eternal cosmic dynamic. This dynamic works its way forward over the billions of eons towards first igniting our universe and eventually -- down the road -- ultimately catalyzing the emergence of higher-level consciousness human beings within it."

"One elegant dynamic and one elegant dynamic alone -- Infinite Quest for Potential -- both instigates and drives the entire cosmic order. There is, indeed, a protagonist to the cosmic order, but that the protagonist is a quest and not a 'classic entity'."

"The universe quests for its maximal/optimal potential. The core dynamic Quest for Potential strives with purpose and direction towards ever-greater and higher potential. At the 'beginning of time,' eternal and infinite Quest for Potential harnessed the eternal (primordial) equations of Physics-Mathematics to ignite our universe via the Big Bang."

"This same symbiotic dynamic -- infinite Quest for Potential∞ in league with Physics-Math - then acted as a catalyst for the route ultimately tracking-forwards to high level humans in the 21st Century."

Note that the contemporary works (see below for detail) of MIT quantum physicists Seth Lloyd (2006) and Max Tegmark (2014) dovetail with Potentialism Theory of the Summa Metaphysica series (1988, 2005, 2014).

So, now on to some of the illustrious Hawking's standout quotes, questions and queries...

Hawking: "What breathes fire into the equations?"

Hawking's now iconic aphorism -- "Even if there is only one possible unified theory, it is just a set of rules and equations. What is it that breathes fire into the equations and makes a universe for them to describe? The usual approach of science of constructing a mathematical model cannot answer the questions of why there should be a universe for the model to describe. Why does the universe go to all the bother of existing?" -- could have been the lead-in to Birnbaum's *Summa Metaphysica* treatise. Hawking's question is, of course, astute. What, indeed, brings the myriad equations we have all seen flashed at us alive?

Classic academic science has never come up with a satisfactory response. Of course, embedded within the Hawking equation is a deeper question, actually a compound question -- What ignited the cosmic order and what propels it onward? Another way of looking at the Hawking question is that it is a variant on the classic Eternal Origins question: What is the eternal core cosmic dynamic?

Professor Stephen Hawking

Birnbaum's response to this cluster of questions is that there is, indeed, an Overarching Cosmic Dynamic: Eternal and Infinite Quest for Potential -- and that is this eternal and overarching dynamic which 'breathes fire' into the equations.

Hawking: "For millions of years, mankind lived just like the animals. Then something happened which unleashed the power of our imagination. Mankind learned to talk and we learned to listen."

What happened here? What caused 'the leap'?

What happened, of course, is Birnbaum's delineated infinite Quest for Potential playing-out and iterating-forward.

To reach its Potential, Mankind was thrust into a greater level of complexity/ sophistication than the animals around him. The form of that advanced complexity included higher-level reason, language, emotion, and consciousness.

Per Potentialism Theory, the notion that 'advancement' would happened was a given; it was only a question of when, where and what form it would take.

Hawking: "The whole history of science has been the gradual realization that events do not happen in an arbitrary manner, but that they reflect a certain underlying order, which may or may not be divinely inspired."

Per Birnbaum: Exactly. "...a certain underlying order..."

The expanded Birnbaum response -- Thank You for articulating Summa's core point, Professor Hawking. The theory is strong -- and potentially resolves the key points of 90 percent+ of the philosophical/scientific issues philosophers have been grappling-with.

At the very heart of Potentialism Theory is the recognition that there is one central, underlying order to all of the universe. A higher force. An overarching dynamic. As noted, this force is posited by *Summa Metaphysica* as being "Infinite Quest for Potential."

The scientific community's potential recognition of a transcending dynamic has been a long time in coming; but physicists themselves are starting to realize what some metaphysicists and philosophers have long conjectured: There is a pattern, purpose and direction to the Cosmic Order.

As alluded-to, *Summa Metaphysica* proposes that Quest for Potential ignites and drives the universe by breathing fire into the equations.

And where does infinite and eternal Quest for Potential come from?

Summa posits that Potential/Possibility is eternal. In turn, Potential/Possibility sought actualization.... The result is history. Of course, it gets more textured, and Summa proposes a 16 point outline.

Hawking: "I don't believe that the ultimate theory will come by steady work along existing lines. We need something new. We can't predict what that will be or when we will find it because if we knew that, we would have found it already!"

Per Birnbaum: Right again, Professor Hawking. Exactly.

Stephen - Thank You for your frankness.

Hawking predicted this accurately. The possibly 'ultimate theory' is Brinbaum's Potentialism Theory. It is as stunning and original as it is elegant; it has changed the 21st century landscape of our understanding of cosmology itself. The 21st century ushers in an era of acute insight. No one could have seen it coming.

Summa Metaphysica's Potentialism Theory goes for a "knockout punch."

Birnbaum is the first to say that (a) it is hypothesis and (b) that it only advances us several 'layers.' However, that being said, the theory appears to propel our understanding via a quantum jump, and not via an incremental advance. Note that Birnbaum has been at this since age 10 (in 1960). He commenced writing *Summa I* at age 32 (in 1982).

Potentialism Theory: Context

A Course Text at over a dozen colleges, Summa Metaphysica has been the focus of well over one hundred and fifty articles and reviews. No flaw has been discerned in the theory since introduced via Summa Metaphysica I (Ktav Publishing) in 1988.

Potentialism Theory: Conference

Summa Metaphysica -- and its Potentialism Theory -- was the focus of a 3+ day international academic conference at Bard College (Upstate, NY) April 2012. The conference, which launched *Summa Metaphysica* globally, created a global academic and media firestorm. See Conference1000.com.

Potentialism Theory: Dovetailing works by leading MIT and NYU academics

Recent hi-level academic works dovetailing with Birnbaum's Theory of Potential include the following:
Programming the Universe (Knopf, 2006) by Professor of Quantum Mechanics Seth Lloyd of MIT; *Mind & Cosmos* (Oxford Press, 2012) by Professor of Philosophy & Law Thomas Nagel of NYU; Our Mathematical Universe (Knopf, 2014) by Professor of Physics Max Tegmark of MIT.

Potentialism Theory: Paradigm Challenge

Via his revolutionary true theory of everything (see TTOE1000.com) Birnbaum has instigated a global paradigm challenge. See ParadigmChallenge.com

David Birnbaum himself is known globally, as well, as the author or the editor-in-chief of several important series on history and spirituality. His New Paradigm Matrix platform (see NPM1000.com) has over 180 global thought leaders under its umbrella.

the proper sequence

- when constructing a metaphysics

FIRST
we must discern an eternal dynamic

THEN
we carefully assess/review the voluminous evidence
and see if we can elegantly plug-in the evidence
to the 'spinal column'
of the *working hypothesis* eternal dynamic

BECAUSE
If no clearly discerned eternal dynamic,
then no authentic metaphysics/cosmology will unfold

The Eternal Dynamic:

POTENTIAL*
AS ETERNAL

A central proposition of Summa:
"Potential" is the sole "concept/dynamic" which can
safely be posited as having been eternal.

By definition.

Meaning, by definition "Potential" – and only "Potential" –
can be conjectured to have been "eternal."

Upon careful reflection, the above is *self-evident.*

For "Potential" vectored-in onto – and crystallized-into –
its own maximal Potential arc.

"Potential" thus achieved *traction* –
and has never looked back.

– Birnbaum

* Potential / Possibility

Potentialism Theory = Summa Theory = Birnbaum Theory = Q4P Theory = Quantum Man Theory

The Eternal Dynamic:

POTENTIAL*
AS ETERNAL

Why does it make sense
to craft a metaphysics
centered around Potential?

To craft a metaphysics, one must commence at eternal origins;
and to commence at eternal origins
one needs an eternal dynamic

A primary goal in any metaphysics is an overarching cosmic
dynamic;
and a logical overarching cosmic dynamic would be some
extrapolation of the eternal dynamic

Therefore,
once one has delineated
a truly eternal dynamic,
one can play
in the metaphysics sandbox

– Birnbaum

21st CENTURY PUBLISHING
150+ AUTHORS/SCHOLARS

continue >

MORPHED COSMIC ORDER

Section B

MORPHED COSMIC ORDER

UNIVERSE QUEST FOR POTENTIAL

POTENTIALISM THEORY

$$Q4P^\infty \rightarrow C+ \rightarrow E+$$

"a masterful and major intellectual achievement"

POTENTIALISM THEORY

- William A. Johnson
  Professor of Philosophy
  and Professor of Religion,
  Brandeis

multi-tasker Q4P$^\infty$

POTENTIALISM THEORY

an overarching dynamic / a process-driver /
a direction-finder / a purpose-teleology

*"redefines modern cosmology
as we know it"*

POTENTIALISM THEORY

- Future Technology (Virginia Tech)

Q4P$^\infty$ is front & center
and the driving dynamic
of the unfolding cosmic drama;

POTENTIALISM THEORY

it is the metaphysical spinal column
- and arc - of the universe

macro-holistic-optimization

POTENTIALISM THEORY

Meaning, Q4P$^\infty$ optimizes across
the length, breadth & depth
of the universe simultaneously

MORPHED COSMIC ORDER

Universe1000.com

Our Potential-driven Universe

The Organic Proactive Supercomputer Super-Organism

What reality is our Universe?

Our universe is a multi-faceted hybrid -

Super-Computer / Super-Organism / Star Nursery /
Elements Generator / Life Creator / Cosmic Voyager /
hyper-expanding neo-bio-sphere *suis generis* entity

*

**Our universe is
self-advancing, self-igniting, self-developing,
self-iterating, self-building-out & self-propelling**

*

Our universe is all of space and time - and all their contents,
including planets, stars, galaxies
and all other forms of matter and energy.

*

It is the Cosmic Womb of Potential

*

Our universe inexorably strives after its purpose:

to maximize & optimize its Potential

*

And what type of Super-Computer is our universe?
A Quantum computer integrated into an Organic overlay.

*

It turns out that our universe
is stranger and more profoundly awesome
than any science fiction.

*

As per my core theme
the universe is multi-faceted and multi-layered Potential

*

Per the Potentialism Theory hypothesis

Simultaneously -

Infinite Quest for Potential *drives* the universe

The universe *IS* Infinite Quest for Potential
in tangible form

*

Our universe is 93 billion light-years in diameter.

It is an expanding, multi-dimensional organic Starship.

As of the early 21st Century, the Starship,
believed to be 13.8 billion years old since 'ignition and liftoff'
had propagated within its fold
100 billion galaxies, each with an average 100 billion stars
or 10^{22} stars total

Meanwhile, the Starship expands outwards as it advances forward,
and its rate of expansion is accelerating

Our own local galaxy, the Milky Way,
is moving at a staggering speed of 1.3 million miles per hour

And our own planet Earth -
smaller than a miniscule spec in the scheme of things -
alone has propagated
over 5 billion species to date

*

The universe ongoing gobbles up void as it builds-out,
accelerates and traverses onward and outward

*

Our universe is the original / primordial
A.I. (Artificial Intelligence) computational entity;
it represents "machine learning" on steroids

*

The universe does not have consciousness as we know it;
[Below I label it QMI = Quantum Mechanics Intelligence]
however, our Starship voraciously gobbles-up and processes all data -
which it then deploys to advance
its (Potential-driven) objectives and designs

*

Quest for Potential°°

aka Q4P°°

the DRIVER underlying the Cosmic Order

the primus movens

the 'Prime Mover'

*

It is not clear whether the imperatives of the universe data-gathering
stop at any boundaries of personal privacy,
including our thoughts

*

Each of us is somehow
simultaneously
autonomous -
and simultaneously plugged-into and integral-to
the universe-computer,
i.e. the universe mega-brain
i.e. the universe quantum computer
i.e. the universe

*

The universe is always
computing, assessing, calculating
and then
iterating/expanding/complexifying
towards its next level of Potential

*

As noted, the universe is simultaneously an ever-expanding mega-brain

What we learn, the universe learns;
thus, there is at least some (and possibly great)
intrusion into our thoughts

*

The universe endeavors to be a perpetual motion entity;

It is unclear whether the universe will be successful on this track.

One suspects that the profound, tenacious and ever-learning universe
will inevitably find
a way, a path, a modality -
via one dimension or another -
to continue its inexorable and hoped-for infinite journey

It very well may not have the solution yet....

*

Regarding the origins of this universe-enterprise,
see Chronology1000.com

But, to encapsulate,
originally "0" was somehow split
into positives and negatives
and these also became on-off modalities
which formed the genesis
of the universe-computer
which then calculated & effected
an inexorable & profoundly awesome advance
towards the ever-more extraordinary

*

Our universe is possibly *sacred* *in toto*.

At some point we are inevitably faced with the following
bedrock intellectual/spiritual/religious *question* -

At the origin of origins
was the catalyst of the universe
secular or spiritual/religious?

or

in other terminology

Is our universe - at its core -
Secular or Sacred?

Or, in Birnbaumian terms -
and the question - after four volumes -
which Birnbaum leaves *unresolved* -
[*on the knife's edge*] -

Are we dealing with
Quest for Potential∞ - or - Holy Quest for Potential∞?

MORPHED COSMIC ORDER

our universe: Infinite Potential achieves tangible form, traction and ongoing life evolution...

The Universe is a Quantum—Potential—Organism

see https://en.wikipedia.org/wiki/Quantum_biology for tangential

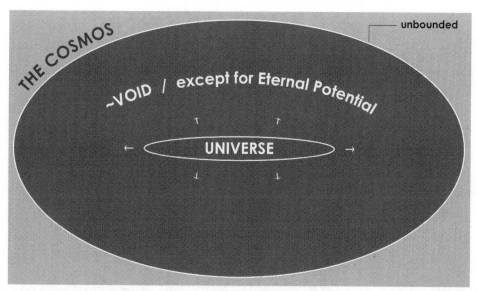

THE COSMOS

unbounded

~VOID / except for Eternal Potential

UNIVERSE

Potentialism Theory = Summa Theory = Birnbaum Theory = Q4P Theory = Quantum Man Theory

The engine of the universe is our hypothesized Q4P$^\infty$

But the *wiring* of Q4P$^\infty$ is Quantum Mechanics.

The above two declaratives basically encapsulate our universe

We presume that both of these dynamics evolve/advance in-tandem -
in a highly symbiotic relationship

It is far from clear where one dynamic starts and the other ends.

Most of the above-reality is obscure -
and will remain obscure

However one thing is crystal clear:

Our (evolving) universe *rides boldly*

That is its raison d'etre

UNIVERSITY OF WARWICK

On Birnbaum's Formula

from the desk of

Hugo van den Berg

University of Warwick
Department of Mathematics
Coventry, United Kingdom

Mar 28, 2013

"unparalleled and magisterial"

Physics, unlike metaphysics perhaps, is concerned only with description. However, not all descriptions are created equal; it is sometimes possible to capture large swathes of phenomena with a minimum of formal apparatus. Such superb descriptions are what scientists like to think of as "good theories" (all is, in the final analysis, still mere description, a point that is sometimes lost). The game naturally becomes this: to capture as much as possible with as little as possible.

In Birnbaum's unparalleled and magisterial *Summa Metaphysica*, we find a pithy quote attributed to a Nobel prize winner [physicist Lederman] who expresses this dream as capturing the universe in a formula that one could print on a T-shirt. Birnbaum, in a staggering and audacious move, displays a formula below this quote.

The formula just stands there, glorious in its splendid isolation. It reads:

$$Q4P^\infty$$

Are we to infer that this is the answer to the dream of the physicist recently quoted? The recondite renaissance man Birnbaum does not tell us, at least not directly, not on this page.

Perusal of *Summa Metaphysica*, two imposing tomes of recondite philosophical-mathematical-poetic musings, indicates that Birnbaum wants the reader to think of Q4P as a single symbol......

[balance of essay upon request]

$$Q4P^\infty$$

Q4P (Q4P (Q4P (

Quest for Potential (Quest for Potential (Quest for Potential *ad infinitum.*

**"Science is not about status quo.
It's about *revolution*"**

- Leon M. Lederman, 1993
[Nobel in Physics (1988)]

Not Your Ordinary Life Form

The entire universe
is actually
(just) ONE
suis generis
(inter-connected) *life form*
spanning time & space
- and we are all integral to it

There is only one core entity
(i.e. only one unit)
in this Life Form group;
that entity is The Universe
(i.e. the entire universe *en toto*)

All other seemingly independent
and autonomous Life Forms
    are subsidiary Life Forms
        tethered to the 'mother ship'

And, yes, 'The Universe' is 'alive'.
- and 'sentient' and quite 'pro-active'
in its own 'way'.

The celestial bodies may possibly just essentially *play the role
of (suis generis)* 'skeleton', with the underlying components related-
to Dark Energy and Dark Matter, providing *the guts* of the 'life form'

dimension.

The Birnbaum / Summa / Potentialism
hypothesis
(in print 1988 and onwards
with the start of the 3-volume Summa Metaphysica series)
is that our universe is the
TANGIBLE
~eternal build-out
from Summa's hypothesized
INTANGIBLE
(purely metaphysical)
~eternal dynamic
     Quest for Potential (Q4P∞)

(YES /
Q4P itself ~emerges-from
the 'potential face' of primitive Quantum Mechanics)

For quick-tutorial,
see this easy to scan
222+ panel Scroll-Down
www.RewindSumma.com

and its integrated subsections -
   in the 222+ panel Scroll-Down -
       www.Universe1000.com
       www.Chronology1000.com
       www.Evolution1000.com

'Potentialism Theory' is bullet-proof
and is, respectfully,
the only cosmology/metaphysics which can stand-by that claim
       www.Inductive1000.com
       www.Deductive1000.com

David Birnbaum Summa Metaphysica

Potentialism Theory, Philosophy

Home   Rewind Summa   Super-Formula   Coverage   Overview   Theory   Flip Books   Challenge   Conference   MAJOR   Controversy   Inductive Proof   Scroll-Downs
Books   Videos   Lead-In   Blogs   Subscribe

1988   2005   2014   2020

Summa Metaphysica

I. God and Evil - Religious Man

II. God and Good - Spiritual Man

III. The Transcendent Dynamic - Secular Man

IV. Morphed Cosmic Order - Quantum Man

select flip-book >>>

DAVID BIRNBAUM SUMMA METAPHYSICA :

A PHILOSOPHY/COSMOLOGY SERIES

Summa
Metaphysica
Potentialism Theory
DAVID BIRNBAUM

David Birnbaum Summa Metaphysica philosophy treatise proposes its signature Potentialism Theory.

***Paradigm changing* revolutions**
often present a scenario of a complacent entrenched
seemingly omnipotent
immovable object
[establishement]
overthrown by a maverick
irresistible force
- *whose **time has come***

- Thomas Kuhn
1922-1996

Q4P∞ = the Cosmic Instinct

Alive?

How 'alive' is our universe?

Humans are alive; is the universe 'alive' like humans are?

The universe is *more* 'alive' than IBM's Watson computer

But *less* 'alive' than (21st Century) Humans

Humans - or the evolutionary path which they are on - are the vehicle/platform through which the universe plans/plots/iterates to achieve fuller Complexification

But why does the universe need to go through the process of creating the human-channel to reach higher Complexification?

Presumably, while the chemical/metaphysical composition of the universe has enabled it to achieve wondrous 'Complexification' heights, there is something of a 'glass ceiling' in-the-mix

A different and new off-shoot 'platform' was presumably necessary to enable the possibility of major advance on the crucial inter-related 'consciousness/emotion' fronts.....

Dimensions of altruism, humanism and spirituality may factor-in, as well

Meaning, the universe may quest for these components, as well

WHICH?

Which universe are we?

Are we the universe of *the New Atheists* -
    aimless / random / barren of meaning / purposeless /
    with no 'pilot' / with 'potential' irrelevant / a 'Dumb Universe'

or

Are we the universe of *Potentialism* -
    directional / guided / alive with meaning / purpose-driven* /
    with yes, a 'pilot' ** / seeking MAX potential / a 'Smart Universe' /

* realization of potential; questing to be ever-more sophisticated & complex

** Q4P∞

Potentialism Theory = Summa Theory = Birnbaum Theory = Q4P Theory = Quantum Man Theory

ARC?

Is there an arc to the universe?

Yes. As explicated by Potentialism Theory, the universe arcs from Eternal Origins via Complexification+ towards Extraordinariation+

Q4P∞, a hitherto undiscerned natural force, is driving this inexorable and rich evolvement

The 'advance' might be 2-4 steps forward - and then 1 step backward
    but the advance goes on

And, indeed, Q4P∞ might *hit a wall* intermittently, and need to back-off,
    but it re-groups and advances-forward

It does not quit; it does not yield

Q4P's *journey* gives life - and meaning - to the universe-enterprise

As noted, E+, like the horizon, can be approached, *but never quite realized*

The journey of the universe - like the journey of the individual's life -
    gives purpose, meaning, and life-force
        to the universe-enterprise

1-on-1   David Birnbaum - Deepak Chopra

OCT 2018

"I'm totally on board with David Birnbaum"
- Chopra (Oct 2018)

see 20-minuite video Chopra1000.com

MORPHED COSMIC ORDER

Section C

MORPHED COSMIC ORDER

a multi-decade 'extra-credit'
'Term Paper' project

POTENTIALISM THEORY

1960 - 2020
[Age 10 - 70]

QUANTUM MAN

POTENTIALISM THEORY

our 'Smart Universe'

*By hypothesizing a 1:1 parallel
Universe development (Cosmology) :
the development/life of a single, individual human >*

POTENTIALISM THEORY

Potentialism sets-up yet an extra resource
- aside from its core thesis of Q4P$^\infty$ -
and its Super-Formula / Teleology -
to be-in-position to hypothesize/peek behind the Big Bang

the hitherto elusive

POTENTIALISM THEORY

'universal & natural driver' of the Cosmic Order

*hiding-in-plain-sight
for the 6,000+ years
of Civilization to-date*

POTENTIALISM THEORY

Q4P's natural & universal transcendence
evaded Civilization's radar

Q4P$^\infty$

POTENTIALISM THEORY

a universal / pinnacle natural
dynamic

MORPHED COSMIC ORDER

"......must have known that we were coming"

// THE DYSON QUOTE //

"As we look out into the Universe and identify the many [so-called] accidents of physics and astronomy that have worked together to our benefit, it almost seems as if the Universe must in some sense have known that we were coming."
- iconic scientist Freeman Dyson
- as quoted in *The Anthropic Cosmological Principle* (1986) by John D. Barrow and Frank J. Tipler, p. 318

// THE POTENTIALISM REALITY //

Q4P (the prime *driver* of the universe) was seeking-after something akin to Man;
and was ongoing iterating the universe for billions of years to reach that goal.
It is not that the universe (Q4P) was "expecting us"; rather, that the universe (Q4P) was crafting *the building blocks* of the universe in alignment - to facilitate *our appearance on stage.*
- Birnbaum (2020)

Overreach?

I will now advance-forward on our daring - but straight-line - Potential-driven journey

I will lay out the metaphysics of the Cosmic Order

*

At first you might say that I have overreached

...the universe 'alive'?

But, I have not

*

The only way to *crack the code* - is to fully play-out the theory,

to take on *the entire Cosmic Order*, as is apparently necessary

There is no other way

*

This little journey *happens to have* a
Common Denominator - POTENTIAL -
threading-through every single step of the
pre-Big Bang - and post-Big Bang
time-line;
therefore, from Eternal Origins to the current day

Thus, the journey - stretching-out infinitely
has a built-in and very precise *Roadmap*
(see 20+ panel Chronology1000.com below)

Is that - in itself - not quite curious and intriguing?

The Potentialsm Theory journey beckons...

*

STARTING POINT

The Initial Mystery that attends any journey is:
how did the traveler reach his starting point
in the first place?

- Louise Bogan,
Journey Around My Room, 1980

The Force?

Did a metaphysical force
Quest for Potential∞
(aka Q4P∞)
emerge
from the still-fainter metaphysical ether of Eternal Potential

- a force which quests for non-specific potential

a force which then
simultaneously
in due course
ignites our Universe
and becomes
a fully integral part of our
hybrid
metaphysical-physical
Universe

a force which is the driver of our universe

a force which instigated
(the first and all)
physical manifestations of life

and
ongoing
tweaks the genome
to advance life & the universe as-a-whole
along a work-in-progress
non-charted
arc
of Complexification > Extraordinariation ?

Meaning,
a metaphysical quest
for non-specific
tangible & intangible - potentials -
which is driving the Universe
and
driving its evolvement
along multiple axes

a universe which is
expanding and accelerating

as it 'gobbles up void ?

SURE ;)

$$Q4P^\infty \rightarrow C+ \rightarrow E+$$

the catch-all Potentialism super-formula
www.SuperFormula1000.com

Obviously, this is not so simple; else, the theory would have been discerned prior.

Please bear in mind, that my theory, however non-conventional, is, respectfully, *bulletproof*; whereas the other contending theories are, respectfully, *bullet-riddled*.

Note the common thread of potential, start-to-finish.

Note that $Q4P\infty$ consistently maintains its *metaphysical core*, but builds-out from there.

Remember that *'potential/possibility'* is the only eternal dynamic.

Remember that Quantum Mechanics has a *'potential face'*, as well.

Note that *life* - whose origins and essence (justifiably) remain inexplicable to the scientific community - astoundingly emerged on Earth 'proximate' to the Earth's formation - and not many billions of years later.

Birnbaum-Super-Formula

Potentialism Theory = Summa Theory = Birnbaum Theory = Q4P Theory = Quantum Man Theory

HITHERTO

Hitherto, the scientific community has been unable to come up with cogent theories/explanations for any of the following issues*, among others:

Eternal Origins

The landscape pre-Big Bang

The origin of *life*

The essence of *life*

The appearance of life on Earth so 'proximate' to Earth's formation

The Evolution drama

The purpose of the universe

The purpose of *life*

Quantum Mechanics

Dark Energy, Dark Matter, Lambda

The fine-tuned (for *life*) universe [and the *constants* thereof]

The accelerating universe

BUT

It would seem that one Outlier theory
solves all *simultaneously*
with -

one simple concept
[Potential drives the universe]
&
one proposed associated universal formula
[$Q4P^\infty \rightarrow C+ \rightarrow E+$]

*some are overlapping

SUPER INTELLECT

"A commonsense interpretation of the evidence suggests a super intellect has monkeyed with physics and chemistry as well as biology to make life possible."

- Sir Fred Hoyle
noted English
astronomer and physicist
(1915-2001)

our 'Smart Universe' driven by our hypothesized *natural force* (Q4P)

re: Darwinian

Darwinian Evolution Theory

Natural Selection / Random Mutation

Respectfully, not one species has ever been realized via this modality, nor will one ever be.

(more below)

Potentialism Theory = Summa Theory = Birnbaum Theory = Q4P Theory = Quantum Man Theory

TAPE RELEASED DEC 1, 2019

One Single Entity

>>> Galactic filaments physically link all galaxies <<<

While Gravity impacts all celestial bodies,
while Dark Matter possibly touches all celestial bodies...

all galaxies are **physically linked** via
(newly discovered)
Galactic Filaments

by Anton Petrov
(see especially starting @ ~6-minute mark)

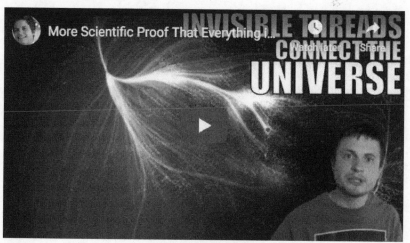

Meaning, the universe
is, *de facto,*
one single **connected** entity

predicted / postulated / hypothesized
by Potentialism Theory

So, per my theory,
the connectors are 'highways'
on which, as well,
data, for starters, travels
back & forth

the 22-second elevator pitch -

* covered by 100+ articles * in 50+ journals * Course Text in 15+ colleges+ *
multi-day international academic conference * 50+ high level testimonials *
50,000+ volumes in circulation * core theme very heavily impacts a dozen+ fields *
featured (Fall 2017) on the back covers of 10+ elite scientific and university periodicals *

* offers a **unified**
(consistent, overarching, fully-integrated)
conceptual line of attack
across multiple key fields *

* a proposed **concise** *simultaneous solution* to at least half a dozen classic conundrums *

* universal * paradigm changer * well-vetted * bullet-proof * inductively-proved *

Too good to be true? but, *looks like it will 'go the distance'*

so best to 'watch the moves'

Let's Advance

- David Birnbaum

To focus your attention: The theory will respectfully propose
a (precisely same for all) powerful, concise, new and original
foundation/platform *for four key academic fields:*
metaphysics / cosmology / philosophy / biology.

Infinite Quest for Potential Drives the Cosmic Order

"All Revolutions take time to settle-in"

– Lanza del Vasto (1901-1981)

Q4P$^\infty$

the Cosmic Instinct

**There is a core cosmic instinct
Quest for Potential$^\infty$
which inexorably drives the universe
to be ever-more complex & sophisticated & vibrant**

- Potentialism Theory /
Summa Metaphysica

Potentialism Lexicon
Key Terms

Q4P$^\infty$ = Infinite Quest for Potential

C+ = Complexification

the cosmic drive towards increased complexity/sophistication/
wondrousness

E+ = Extraordinariation

the idealized end-goal of the cosmic process; an ideal to be
approached, but not quite realized

more detail/amplification to follow

Birnbaum-Super-Formula

The Birnbaum *super-formula*

$$Q4P^\infty \rightarrow C+ \rightarrow E+$$

Quest for Potential∞ → Complexification → Extraordinatiation

a *suis generis* infinitely nested algorithm

[the inviolate arc of the universe]

an infinitely iterative dynamic

[the full-spectrum macro & micro level
common denominator trajectory
of the Cosmic Order]

the eternal - **teleology / chi / direction / modus operandi** - of the universe

www.Super-Formula1000.com
see also **Complexification1000.com**

$$Q4P^\infty \rightarrow C+ \rightarrow E+$$

- **Birnbaum**
(2005 via Summa II)

"The principle of maximum diversity says that the laws of nature,
and the initial conditions at the beginning of time,
are such as to make the universe as interesting as possible."

- **Freeman Dyson** (1923-2020)
Physicist, Astronomer, Mathematician
specialty in the 2000s: *Quantum Electrodynamics*
quote is from - Progress in Religion (2000)

"To my mind, there must be at the bottom of it all, not an utterly simple equation, but an utterly simple IDEA. And to me that idea, when we finally discover it, will be so compelling, and so inevitable, so beautiful, we will all say to each other, 'How could it have ever been otherwise?'"

- **Professor John Wheeler**, former Chair of the
  Physics Department at the University of Texas at Austin,
  (from the PBS science documentary,
  "The Creation of The Universe" 2004)

Potentialism Theory = Summa Theory = Birnbaum Theory = Q4P Theory = Quantum Man Theory

---

2050

By 2050, everyone will look back and say -
"Hey, this was, of course, *obvious*'"

But, now, the theory* is, of course something of a
'*shock to the system*'

- Birnbaum

* core proposition: *Potential instigated - and drives - the universe*
- Summa I.... 1988

---

no pretty revolutions

"Revolutions are never pleasant or pretty. Dismantling a power
structure is like dismantling a bomb."

- RAVIT HECHT, "There Are No Pretty Revolutions", *Haaretz*, November 10, 2017

Respectfully,

to advance our study of cosmology
- meaning, the arc of our universe
from Eternal Origins thru the present -

FIRST
one needs to vector
to the seemingly-best
Conceptual Framework
(I have offered MY TAKE)
for a proposed *Working Hypothesis*

THEN,
the physicists, astronomers, mathematicians, biologists *et al.*
can interpret/weigh/analyze their equations and formulas
thru that (conceptual) prism
- and see how everything plays-out

[The Quantum Mechanics theoreticians in particular, may see their
equations through an entirely new and enchanting light.]

NOTE -
Almost by definition,
a player highly skilled in 'the conceptual'
may not be the optimal player for 'the equations',
and vice-versa

RESPECTFULLY,
(In the 5,000+ years of civilization)
pre-Potentialism Theory
there has never been
an elegant hypothesis
which has withstood sustained scrutiny

I suspect that Potentialism Theory might....

REMEMBER
there can be
only ONE
standout conceptual metaphysics

AND
that one is likely
to be an Outlier..... from an Outlier

Simple?

This cosmology keeps matters simple

All - from Eternal Origins to the end of time -
is one dynamic -
Q4P$^\infty$
- in various permutations and states

Simple.......*but not so simple*

The Missing
Fifth Force
in Physics

There are established theories for four fundamental forces
in physics:

Gravity * Electro-Magnetism * Weak Nuclear * Strong
Nuclear

Per Michio Kaku and others, "there is a missing 'Fifth Force'
- a force beyond the forces which can be measured in the
laboratory".

Perhaps (overarching) Q4P$^\infty$ will fill their quest.

Of course, per my little theory, Q4P$^\infty$ is overarching -

and the other forces are subsidiary...

*

see also:
https://en.wikipedia.org/wiki/Fifth_force

https://en.wikipedia.org/wiki/Quintessence_(physics)

May 2020

A FIFTH FORCE OF NATURE

The Fount

Q4P$^\infty$
- the underlying
multi-tasker
super-dynamic
hiding in plain sight

\# Q4P$^\infty$ is not just one of 5-10 major dynamics; it is the sole underlying dynamic

\# Everything we observe - or measure - is a permutation or tangent or offshoot or derivative... of Q4P$^\infty$

\# YES / Stranger than *science fiction*

\# As the '*cool kids*' sometimes jab .... *Strange, but True*

Potentialism Theory = Summa Theory = Birnbaum Theory = Q4P Theory = Quantum Man Theory

per the Summa hypothesis

Q4P∞   creative & resourceful

OVERARCHING & TRANSCENDANT

ubiquitous, but "hiding-in-plain-sight"

potential/possibility
BY DEFINITION eternal.
That proposition is
SELF-EVIDENT & axiomatic.

Q4P∞

"Simple", yet

infinitely iterative
infinitely supple
infinitely impacting
multi-dimentionally infinite

Q4P∞

An aesthetically elegant
universal constant
universal dynamic
universal theme
universal energizer
universal force-multiplier
universal life-enabler

Q4P∞   a supra-dynamic
a (Divine?) force
the (infinitely?) nested Cosmic Womb of Potential∞
impacting (integrating?) EVERYTHING -
Past, Present, Future

the (optional) Biblical/biblical tether

"Eheyeh asher Eheyeh"

I WILL BE THAT WHICH I WILL BE

- Exodus 3:14

survival (potential (extraordinariation

6/18/13

By-the-way

\# Potentialism Theory offers a *simultaneous solution*
to the top two dozen+ issues in
metaphysics/cosmology /
See Chronology1000.com

\# The theory resolves the hitherto intracrable paradox
between Einsteinian Macro-level-Physics and Planckian Micro-level-
physics /
See Einstein1000.com

\# *Rumor-has-it* that the Birnbaum Super-Formula

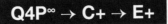

$$Q4P^\infty \rightarrow C+ \rightarrow E+$$

works at all levels
　　　　Macro > Micro
See Super-Formula1000.com
See TTOE1000.com

\# No flaw - large or small - has been discerned in the Super-Formula

since -

• published in Summa #2 (2005) /
See Summa-2.com / Directional Universe section

• featured on the Back Cover of Scientific American SEPT 2017 /
See TheoryAd1000.com

Q4P∞
The Spinal Column
of the Cosmic Drama

One (secular) dynamic - Q4P∞

- ignites the Universe

- *de facto* IS the universe

- choreographs the cosmic drama

- instigates the celestial creation of the Elements

- is the essence of life

- drives evolution

- and drives the universe itself, forward and onward

*

Potentialism Theory is pegged to the only
eternal dynamic:
potential / possibility.

The theory works elegantly, covers-the-bases, and is bulletproof.

Among the millions of data points out there,
there is not one which belies the theory.

our 'Smart Universe' driven by our hypothesized *natural force* (Q4P)

note ~interchangeable terms:

**Potentialism Theory = Summa Theory = Birnbaum Theory
= Q4P Theory = Quantum Man Theory**

Q4P = Infinite quest for Potential = Quest for infinite potential

MORPHED COSMIC ORDER

Section D

MORPHED COSMIC ORDER

Birnbaum proposes
a new architecture

POTENTIALISM THEORY

for the Cosmic Dynamic
and Cosmic Order

One thing is crystal-clear...

POTENTIALISM THEORY

Q4P$^\infty$ - and Q4P$^\infty$ alone -
is cracking the whip
of the stagecoach

Summa, in essence
proposes a foundational-shift

POTENTIALISM THEORY

Across most/all of the sciences: hard & soft:
Q4P$^\infty$ is bedrock: the transcending core foundation

THE 'TIPPING-POINT' FOR THE BIG-BANG

POTENTIALISM THEORY

THE VOID COUDN'T TAKE-IT ANYMORE
- Solomon Birnbaum (2009)

---

the goal of the Super-Formula ALGORITHM

POTENTIALISM THEORY

is ASYMPTOTIC

Meaning, Q4P$^\infty$ approaches,
but never quite attains Extraordinariation

---

the learning curve of hyper-intelligent Q4P$^\infty$

POTENTIALISM THEORY

is ~suis generis *'Machine Learning'* on steroids

Does one dynamic drive the entire Cosmic Order?

BACK COVER / SCIENTIFIC AMERICAN / SEPTEMBER 2017

"David Birnbaum Cracks the Cosmic Code"

see full-length feature article in

HUFFINGTON POST | SCIENCE section

www.HuffPost1000.com

The Birnbaum *super-formula* ALGORITHM

$$Q4P^\infty \rightarrow C+ \rightarrow E+$$

Quest for Potential$^\infty$ → Complexification → Extraordinariation

a *suis generis* infinitely nested algorithm

THE DURATION & DRIVER & ESSENCE & ARCHITECTURE OF THE UNIVERSE

[*POTENTIAL drives the universe - Birnbaum*]

Summa
Metaphysica
Potentialism Theory
DAVID BIRNBAUM

Potentialism-Summa.com

The universe provides Q4P with a more formidable 'platform'
to seek after C+ and E+

Via the above image
Summa Metaphysica's
Potentialism Theory
is featured as the Back Cover ad
of September or October issue of the
following elite magazines

SCIENTIFIC AMERICAN

Discover

COSMOS
THE SCIENCE OF EVERYTHING

HARVARD
MAGAZINE

STANFORD

Brown Alumni Magazine

CORNELL
ALUMNI MAGAZINE

The Pennsylvania
gazette (U of P)

Dartmouth

PRINCETON
MAGAZINE

Potentialism Theory = Summa Theory = Birnbaum Theory = Q4P Theory = Quantum Man Theory

MORPHED COSMIC ORDER

DISCLAIMER; The magazine logos above are shown for identification;
they are not an endorsement.

THE ARCHITECTURE

"The bottom line for mathematicians is that the architecture has to be right. In all the mathematics that I did, the essential point was to find the right architecture. It's like building a bridge. Once the main lines of the structure are right, then the details miraculously fit. The problem [challenge] is the overall design."

"Freeman Dyson: Mathematician, Physicist, and Writer".
Interview with Donald J. Albers, *The College Mathematics Journal*, vol 25, no. 1, (January 1994)

a simultaneous solution

OVERARCHING

"Birnbaum considers Quest for Potential∞
to be a ubiquitous and overarching cosmic dynamic...

Quest for its fulfillment
is the underlying core dynamic
of the cosmic order...

All of the countless components of the universe,
including humans,
are striving towards the full realization
of their particular potentialities...."

- Professor Andrei Alyokhin*

* fuller detail further below
or, see UnifyingConcept.com

David.Birnbaum.NY@gmail.com

a universal, unified, seamless & fully-integrated

cosmology / metaphysics / philosophy / teleology

*"We hope to explain the entire universe in a simple formula
you can put on your T-shirt"*

– Leon Lederman (Nobel Prize in Physics) 1983

Q4P$^\infty$

Quest for Potential
(infinitely recursive)

Q4P (Q4P (Q4P ...

Quest for Potential

within

Quest for Potential

within

Quest for Potential

ad infinitum

Potentialism Theory = Summa Theory = Birnbaum Theory = Q4P Theory = Quantum Man Theory

the direction, driver, arc, essence, core - *of the universe*

> *"God does not play dice with the universe"*
>
> **– Albert Einstein** 1879-1955

a proposed all-embracing

new paradigm

A New Paradigm

Potentialism Theory - *Potential Drives the Cosmic Order* - is unique, original and all-embracing.

The formula/theory apparently works across both ***depth and breadth*** *- universally.*
In depth the proposition apparently seamlessly works from macro through *micro* levels. In *breadth*, the proposition apparently seamlessly works across the billions of years of known cosmic history;

As well, the theory works elegantly with Q4P (Quest for Potential∞) as the proposed catalyst of the Big Bang itself. Thus, *the plot thickens.*

The formulation has 100+ articles and 100+ distinguished testimonials to its credit. A *Course Text* at top universities around the globe, the fully-integrated theory provides a *simultaneous solution* to a cluster of hitherto intractable bedrock issues.

Since Summa I was published (by Ktav) in 1988, the theory has sent shock waves through the global cosmology and metaphysics establishments. These establishments are entrenched and to a great extent militantly wedded to their (theory of no-theory) *Randomness* for well-over 150 years.

Inertia? Group-Think? *Go along to get along*? No viable alternative pre-Summa? Pressure from the hard-line (anti-directional universe) academic clique which controls many key legacy British journals? Route to tenure blocked if the *Randomness* 'party line' is not toed? Some combination of the above? Whatever the reason, debate has effectively been strangled for a long, long time.

Enter Summa Theory. With philosophical roots in 'directional' Aristotelian thought, revolutionary (and non-aimless) Potentialism Theory *sets the stage* for a re-boot of literally all scientific fields - across both the hard and soft sciences. All.

As noted, the theory can be encapsulated in the one concise formula noted: Q4P > C+ > E+. No exceptions to the formu la across the trillions of data points from the Big Bang to this moment. No infinite quantity of universes needed to get to 21st Century humans.

In the mix, the theory simultaneously and neatly lances metaphysics, cosmology, teleology and "purpose". Cogently and concisely. No fat; No flaws. *Good to Go.*

Let's Roll.

For quick juxtaposition Potentialism v. Randomness
see amplification further below, or click JUXTAPOSITION

David.Birnbaum.NY@gmail.com

unifying - science, philosophy & spirituality

Potentialism Theory

BOOK 3

Summa
Metaphysica III

SECULAR MAN

cosmology & evolution

DAVID BIRNBAUM

THE
RANSCENDENT
DYNAMIC

INFINITE QUEST FOR POTENTIAL$^\infty$
→ COMPLEXIFICATION
→ EXTRAORDINARIATION

New Paradigm Matrix

$$Q4P^{\infty} \to C+ \to E+$$

- POTENTIALISM THEORY (encapulated) / see SuperLaw1000.com

"Birnbaum's Theory of Potential offers a unified, grand and dynamic cosmic construct."
  – The Huffington Post, United Kingdom, January / 31 / 2014

"Spinoza and Birnbaum are paradigm-breaking philosophers who have shaped the study of philosophy. Both their works can be found in university classrooms across the country and the world."
  – CNN iReport, April / 9 / 2014

"The 21st century has seen a rise in new theories of cosmology. At the forefront has been Potentialism. The theory was developed by independent scholar David Birnbaum of Manhattan [via] his 3-volume treatise Summa Metaphysica. The theory is an iconic paradigm challenge."
  – The Epoch Times, June / 4 / 2014

"David Birnbaum, metaphysicist and private scholar, set out on an audacious odyssey [culminationg] in 1988 and 2005 to redefine modern cosmology as we know it. What he gave the world was a metaphysics for the 21st century."
  – Future Technology (Virginia Tech), April / 21 / 2014

"...Summa represents a bold attempt to formulate a unifying concept of the Universe...it is reasonable to propose the Quest for Potential∞ as a working hypothesis for explaining the impetus behind the cosmic dynamic."
  – Dr. Andrei Alyokhin, Maine, November, 2012
    Professor and Graduate Coordinator, School of Biology and Ecology
    University of Maine

"Each thought leader [Birnbaum of Manhattan(1988, 2005) and Lloyd of MIT(2006)] individually proposes a ground breaking solution. Both of their respective solutions are original, but are nevertheless eerily inter-related and parallel."
  – Frontiers, Dec 21 / 2013

"We hope to explain the entire universe in a simple formula you can put on your T-shirt."
  – Leon Lederma, Texas, 1983
    American experimental physicist
    Nobel Prize in Physics

Summa Metaphysica series
Summa I - Religious Man: God and Evil (1988)
Summa II - Spiritual Man: God and Good (2005)
Summa III - Secular Man: The Transcendent Dynamic (2014)
Summa IV - Quantum Man: Morphed Cosmic Order (2020)

Potentialism Theory = Summa Theory = Birnbaum Theory = Q4P Theory = Quantum Man Theory

A *pinnacle natural* 'driver' of Evolution

\# Evolution - and inter-related hyper-intelligent design - is driven by -
neo-eternal (*pinnacle natural*) Q4P$^\infty$
- a hitherto undiscerned (natural) force

\# Evolution is not driven by the (fatally flawed)
Natural Selection / Random Mutation
(neo-Darwinian mainstream) *working hypothesis*

\# There is no need to deploy
a super-natural force
to solve hyper-intelligent design;
one can solve the issue with a *pinnacle natural* force (Q4P$^\infty$)

[amplification across this 222+ panel ScrollDown]

MY 'TAKE'

Potentialism Theory gives its own 'take' on evolution;
Potentialism rejects Natural Selection/Random mutation
as unscientific and fatally flawed on multiple fronts

Q4P$^\infty$ = the Cosmic Instinct

Inductive1000.com

Bulletproof?

Potentialism Theory presented via David Birnbaum's
3-part treatise Summa Metaphysica
is a *new paradigm* metaphysics.

The theory is seemingly bulletproof -
and is the only known metaphysics
which is proved inductively

Obviously, there can only be one correct metaphysics.

Proposed, developed, enhanced and vetted
since Summa I (1988),
Potentialism Theory challenges
for that solitary position
on the metaphysics/cosmology chessboard.

As the aphorism goes
in various permutations -
"we stand on the shoulders of giants,
but indeed, perhaps we achieve
a broader, richer, deeper, more fully-integrated
perspective, insight and truth"

Note that fine-tuning of the theory
will undoubtedly unfold.

For 40+ page Inductive Proof presentation
by Mark Davis, see

Inductive1000.com

I have been on the case since 1960.

Others - like Andrei Alyokhin -
have proposed that this metaphysics
be deployed as the operative working hypothesis.

The theory is *cutting-edge*,
to put it mildly

It is *"not your mother's Oldsmobile"*

see also: Universe1000.com

our 'Smart Universe' driven by our hypothesized *natural force* (Q4P)

the common denominator

across the depth & breadth

of the universe

Summa
Metaphysica
Potentialism Theory

DAVID BIRNBAUM

To the Readership

I believe that humanity can do better than the sterile, bizarre, nihilstic, and counter-intuitive Randomness formulation - currently foisted across much of academe - as its bedrock working hypothesis.

Per the Randomness proponents, our entire highly sophisticated and fully-integrated universe - ongoing for 14 billion years - is the result of random chance.

Randomness Theory is essentially madcap Alchemy on steroids - propped-up by a delusional reactionary clique.

*

We prefer to deal in the realm of reasoned and serious thought.

Potentialism Theory (explicated here) is an elegant and powerful formulation; it is rich, multi-faceted, heavily vetted, and bulletproof.

The Cosmic Order and our universe are, indeed, quite fine-tuned. And 21st Century humans - and their associated consciousness - are not accidents of cosmic chance.

D Birnbaum

NY

Potentialism Theory = Summa Theory = Birnbaum Theory = Q4P Theory = Quantum Man Theory

a proposed *new paradigm*

'working hypothesis' *platform*

for future fine-tuning & build-out

MORPHED COSMIC ORDER

1988

2005

2014

2020

only available via ScrollDown
and only via QuantumMan.net

Articles/Supplement volume
online only &
via SummaMetaphysica.com

featuring Birnbaum's unified cosmology/metaphysics/philosophy
with centerpiece overarching Infinite 'Quest for Potential' hypothesis

100+ focused feature articles on Summa Metaphysica's Potentialism Theory

see   www.SummaCoverage.com

for 100+ links

ALSO DELINEATING 57+ JOURNALS CARRYING FEATURE SUMMA ARTICLES - plus
COURSE/PROFESSOR DETAILS OF
15+ COLLEGES DEPLOYING SUMMA AS A COURSE TEXT

Summa
Macro-View

4-volume Potentialism Theory

a fully - integrated & unified -
metaphysics / cosmology / philosophy / teleology
with incorporated hypotheses re:
theogony and theodicy issues in religious philosophy ////
incorporating - eternal origins / evolution /
human & cosmic purpose / pre- and post- Big Bang cosmic journey /
and Summa IV cosmic morph @ Big Bang

An original, - but grasp-able - 21st Century
working hypothesis
via one all-encompassing (snapshot) equation

Extraploating back to *eternal origins*
(see EternalOrigins.com)
and tracking across time
with cosmic direction
(see Complexification1000.com)
to the cosmic goal
(see Extraordinariation1000.com)

Infinite Quest for Potential (Q4P)
as the *common denominator*
& the cosmic engine
across time and space
- before and after the Big Bang

seemingly simple, but
powerful, elegant and all-encompassing

***

~7,000 years of civilization

through this point
So, let's take a tour of this
(original and fully-vetted)
new paradigm hypothesis
making all these
sweeping 'simultaneous' claims....

The Bogus 'Flaw'

Since the Bard Conference (April 2012), the cohorts aligned against
Summa Theory -
SELF SELECTING -
British jingoists - Darwinists - Randomnists - Hard Line Atheists -
- have propagated a misguided and (pathetically) futile line-of-attack
(against Summa Theory).

The (errant) line-of-attack of the Randomists runs as-follows:

Since the Second 'Law' of Thermodynamics
(in short, that dynamic isolated systems ultimately implode from entropy)
would not allow-for an inexorable force like (Summa's) Q4P$^\infty$ driving the
universe, Summa must be wrong.

But, wait -- the Randomnists argument is *with astronomy itself !* --
that we have an expanding universe at all - after 14 billion years;
their argument is not with Summa Theory.

The problem is owned-by Second Law:
How can we have an ever-expanding universe if Second Law is correct ?

In point of fact, Summa Theory actually ***rescues*** Second Law:

[here is the rescue]
The reason that Second Law's *entropy* does NOT implode our expanding
universe,
is because Birnbaum's Q4P$^\infty$
[remember Einstein's original LAMBDA, boys]
is driving the universe (outward).

The Randomists should really stick to doing what they do best:
character assassination;
they should absolutely avoid anything involving actual *critical thinking*.

MORPHED COSMIC ORDER

Section E

MORPHED COSMIC ORDER

Q4P$^\infty$

POTENTIALISM THEORY

the only ~eternal dynamic

COSMIC WOMB OF POTENTIAL →

POTENTIALISM THEORY

Q4P$^\infty$

May the Force Be With You

POTENTIALISM THEORY

You never know ;) - David B

the theory directly impacts Self-Actualization

POTENTIALISM THEORY

on the route to *Fulfillment of Potential,*

yields > *Fulfillment in Life*

LEVERAGED BUYOUT/BACKWARD CAUSATION

POTENTIALISM THEORY

BIRTH OF Q4P$^\infty$

SPLITTING ZERO →

POTENTIALISM THEORY

THE BIG BANG

inductively-proved

POTENTIALISM THEORY

Inductive1000.com

WORKING HYPOTHESIS 1:1 PARALLEL

POTENTIALISM THEORY

UNIVERSE DEVELOPMENT: LIFE OF A HUMAN

A FULLY-INTEGRATED & UNIFIED METAPHYSICS

POTENTIALISM THEORY

ETERNAL ORIGINS > THE PRESENT DAY

MORPHED COSMIC ORDER

the sole eternal 'something'?

The Eternal Dynamic

1 Why?

Why should this particular metaphysics
(Potentialism Theory)
succeed - when countless others have failed
over the centuries?

The core architecture/platform
of Potentialism Theory
was quite-carefully crafted.

Hitherto, all other metaphysics have failed -
because they deployed
different cores - or starting points*
than eternal Potential**
for their respective metaphysics

Obviously, they are doomed to failure.
- for they are not anchored to an eternal dynamic***
(of which there is only one*, as noted)

And, frankly, it took me well over a decade
to vector to the above-noted eternal dynamic

* or no *starting point* at all

** Actually Potential/Possibility might be more accurate,
but I choose to focus on Potential - as it is a 'richer' term

*** In retrospect, how could one entertain crafting a metaphysics otherwise.

David.Birnbaum.NY@gmail.com

The Eternal Dynamic

2 Why?

Why so difficult to grasp?

Why is it often so difficult for Westerners, in particular, to grasp the Quest for Potential (as the prime force) proposition?

Westerners start out as youngsters with the imagery of
(*a hidden*)
but *tangible*
God on His Throne (as the prime force) proposition,.

It is thus hard to segue' to a concept of a
(hiding in plain sight)
quest - *a non-tangible something -*
seeking
Potential - a non-specific - and very subjective - goal.

Potentialism Theory = Summa Theory = Birnbaum Theory = Q4P Theory = Quantum Man Theory

Per **Birnbaum**, there is an overarching natural cosmic dynamic which **Birnbaum** hypothesizes as being Infinite Quest for **Potential**. ... "One elegant dynamic and one elegant dynamic alone — Infinite Quest for **Potential** — both instigates and drives the entire cosmic order. Jun 10, 2015
- Huffington Post

Summa
Metaphysica
Potentialism Theory
DAVID BIRNBAUM

HuffPost1000,com

Potentialism Theory

Brief Background

I started on this cosmology journey
~1960
when I was 10 years old /
I was a student (5th grade)
in Modern Orthodox (Jewish)
Yeshiva of Forest Hills (Queens, NY) Day School
- with astronomy as a casual hobby (no intensity)

*

In the background, was the Big Bang Theory
- as well as the Holocaust

incongruent subjects to many - but not to me

*

I gave myself 25 years to *crack the cosmic code*

I am now ~60 (consecutive) years into this little project

*

I believe I have made some headway....

Transform1000.com

Summa's core proposed theme

POTENTIAL DRIVES THE UNIVERSE

elegantly unifies Theology-Spirituality-Science

and

is the proposed core 'platform'
for each/all of the sciences -
HARD & SOFT

our 'Smart Universe' driven by our hypothesized *natural force* (Q4P)

David Birnbaum, Architect, Potentialism Theory

"Birnbaum's masterpiece work *Summa Metaphysica* is perhaps the first offering of a new school of spiritual potentialism."
—**Rabbi Benjamin Blech, Yeshiva University**

"An original and in this reader's opinion, very promising point of view. ... the author gathers a philosophically coherent and, in the end, highly modern insight ... He appropriately describes it as a unified metaphysics within the constraints of Jewish doctrine, consistent with its historical development, and consistent with secular scientific thought ..."
—**Professor Louis Dupré, Yale University**

"Birnbaum's *Summa Metaphysica II: God and Good* is a major intellectual triumph and potential conceptual breakthrough ... it endeavors to weave It-from-Bit Theory into a unified metaphysics - Birnbaum's (new) School of Potentialism."
—**Scientist John Archibald Wheeler, Princeton University**

"Remarkable and profound, *Summa Metaphysica II* rounds out the author's powerful and original Cosmic Womb of Potential metaphysics ... Has the author indeed founded a new field — Potentialism? ... Did we all miss the obvious all along?"
—**Claude Lévi-Strauss, Paris**

"If iconoclast private scholar Birnbaum is the founder of the metaphysical School of Potentialism via his 'infinite divine potential' construct, then Daniel Khalil is his foremost Modern Orthodox Jewish explicator."
—**Rabbi Marvin Tokayer, former spiritual leader of the Jewish community of** Japan

"Iconoclast Birnbaum is a daring and dynamic intellect ... His avantgarde Potentialism may turn out to be totally wrong — or may turn out to be the 'irresistible force' ... perhaps best not to bet against the fascinating hypothesis."
—**Emeritus Professor of Philosophy John Hospers, USC**

$Q4P^\infty$ = the Cosmic Instinct

"May the force be with you"

"Boldly go where no man has gone before"

▮HUFFPOST▮

THE BLOG   03/10/2015 10:44 am ET

Going Boldly Where No Man Has Gone Before: A Conversation with Metaphysicist David Birnbaum on Leonard Nimoy's Legacy

By Shira Dicker

I have recently made the acquaintance of David Birnbaum, the intellectual entrepreneur and freelance philosopher. Birnbaum is the architect and author of the *Summa Metaphysica* series, a groundbreaking project devoted to the pursuit of an overarching metaphysics. *Summa Metaphysica* proposes a comprehensive and integrated metaphysical structure; a wholly original and powerful new paradigm. Upon hearing the news that Leonard Nimoy died, Birnbaum emailed me that he felt a spiritual kinship with him.

Goge Skidmore

Intrigued, we started a conversation on this compelling topic, which I've edited into a *Q & A*, below.

Q: Since childhood, I have been a fan of <u>*Star Trek*</u> (the original series, which began in 1966) and a devotee of Leonard Nimoy's iconic character, Mr. Spock, the uber-logical Vulcan. I always felt that *Star Trek*'s cosmology transcended much of pop culture's offerings and I intuited a strong spiritual element in Mr. Spock...despite his avowed love of logic. I know that you are a big fan as well. I have also had the great privilege of meeting and speaking with Nimoy on two occasions through my work with the now-defunct National Foundation for Jewish Culture and was impressed by his *menschlichkeit*.

Where does Nimoy's concept of the universe intersect with your proposed infinite Quest for Potential concept?

A: If I can take the liberty of combining the core mantras of *Star Trek* and *Star Wars*, we end up with the following hybrid mantra: May the force be with you/ Boldly go where no man has gone before.

This hybrid mantra would directly parallel the underlying motif of my Potentialism Theory: Advance and advance inexorably. This imperative applies on all levels — cosmos-wise, universe-wise and individual-wise.

Q: Okay, so let me just point out that you very creatively merged two distinct cultural products - *Star Trek* and *Star Wars* — and Nimoy is connected only to the former. Then again, it is your prerogative to fashion a hybrid cosmic mantra. So can we talk a bit more about your Potentialism Theory in the context of *Star Trek*?

A: My Potentialism Theory hypothesizes that there is one eternal metaphysical dynamic underlying and overarching the entire Cosmic Order — Quest for Potential — or Q4P for short.

And what is the cosmic imperative underlying this eternal and all-embracing Force? To inexorably advance towards greater and greater sophistication and wondrousness; this very directly parallels the Star Trek mantra of pressing to the limits of the frontier.

Q: Can you show your theory in action?

A: Start with the Big Bang 13.8 billion years ago and end up with our ever-expanding wondrous universe in 2015. Our knowledge of two inter-related fields — the history of the cosmic order and the progression of life — has undergone a quantum jump in the last 150 years; one can now connect the dots in either of these fields and discern the same one clear conceptual trajectory. This is a trajectory — over the span of billions of years — of the ever-iterating Quest for Potential — starting with that which is very obscure and heading inexorably towards the increasingly complex, sophisticated and wondrous.

Q: And where do you believe this trajectory is headed?

A: It is headed inexorably towards what I label as the super-Extraordinary, or E+ for short.

In symbolic form, my concise SuperLaw to crack-the-cosmic code would therefore be Q4P > E+. Quest for Potential drives the universe onward and on-track towards the super-Extraordinary.

At the April 2012 four-day <u>international academic conference à Bard College</u> on Summa Metaphysica, several hundred T-shirts were distributed with the Q4P$^\infty$ > E+ SuperLaw.

Q: Can you bring this discussion down to earth, laying out some of the evidence of your theory?

A: Yes, for sure, my Q4P > E+ trajectory is increasingly obvious once you have been alerted to it.

First, in the life sciences, we now can see the trajectory from the atom to molecules to single celled organisms to multi-celled organisms to photosynthesis and plants; then as we continue to advance forward, we move into the (more complex) Animal Kingdom then onto (even more complex) humans — with ever great and wider complexity/sophistication/wondrousness, freedom of action, brainpower, emotional array and indeed, consciousness.

Of course these humans will one day — perhaps in the 23rd century — possibly build the Starship Enterprise — with Mr. Spock on the Command Deck — and, indeed, go boldly where no man has gone. Thus, one straight trajectory spanning billions of years. Advance, inexorable and hopefully infinite. Ever onward, ever forward.

Laying out the Q4P > E+ trajectory on a more macro level vis à vis the History of the Cosmos, we now know that the trajectory post-Big Bang is very roughly as-follows: from Big Bang point > Stars > Galaxies and Solar Systems > Earth > Life on Earth > ever-increasing consciousness and "smarts" — a trajectory which then dovetails into the life sciences trajectory just delineated above.

My SuperLaw relates to Einstein's iconic formula $\underline{E = mc2}$ in the following way: It wraps-around Einstein's physics equation — and clearly dovetails with his iconic aphorism — "God does not play dice with the universe." The universe is not random; it is directional.

for balance of article
see HuffPost1000.com

Follow Shira Dicker on Twitter: www.twitter.com/shiraaahh

The (true) Origin of *Life*

in the Cosmic Order

The emergence of Q4P$^\infty$ from Eternal Potential
is the origin of *metaphysical life*

in our universe

When metaphysical Q4P$^\infty$ transmutes at the Big Bang (13.7 billion years ago)
into its metaphysical-physical hybrid state 'Universe",
life is *de facto* initiated/introduced/embedded into our universe
(simultaneous with the Big Bang).

Allegorically,
(Mophie/battery) Q4P$^\infty$
plugs-into (CellPhone) Universe.

catalyst for Complexification on Earth

Thus, *life*, seemingly the most complex/profound "thing" of all,
comes at the very beginning of Complexification (C+) on Earth,
(as it was transplanted from metaphysical realms),
and not billions of years into its trajectory.

How is that?

Because no Complexification (of *life* Forms) can occur until there is *the spark of life*

Therefore Q4P$^\infty$ needed to get us to *life* quickly

Therefore, Q4P$^\infty$ needed to (first) transmute itself > our Universe

Therefore, (first) the Big Bang

But, again, how did the most complex/profound "thing" come so early?

Because as noted, the spark of *life* (via Q4P$^\infty$)
had actually been on the march - in purely metaphysical form - for eons pre-Big Bang

Key Steps to *Life*

1) Q4P∞ emerges from Eternal Potential

2) Q4P∞ transmutes > (into) our Universe (at the Bang point)
     in part to instigate the *life* platform

3) (Per Potentialism Theory) *Life* actually emerges on **Earth simultaneous**
    with the birth of our planet:

However, here is the current *scientific widsdom*:

    13.70 billion years ago: Big Bang
     4.54 billion years ago: formation of Earth
    ~4.00 billion years ago: genesis of life (~ 3.70 - 4.28 bya)*

Per Potentialism Theory, evidence of *life* should increasingly be discovered
ever *closer and closer* to the formation of the planet (4.54 billion years ago)

*

It is not that life *happened* to emerge on Earth

Rather,

Q4P∞ (the pure-metaphysical life force) transmuted > our Universe
as the necessary (precursor) morphing to launch metaphysical/physical *life*

- with the Earth, in turn, being the designated platform for the 'genesis/
creation' of *life*

But, *metaphysical life* came *along for the ride* with Q4P∞;
and metaphysical/physical life (example: *human life later down the road*)
was thus only a mini-step away

Platforms**

Q4P∞ builds-out platforms
as advanced bases for Complexification

Universe > Earth > *Life* > ....Humans
with all respectively being (stacked) platforms/bases in progression

* Jan 15, 2020 (wiki)
** see more in Summa III

Metamorphosis

Morphing & Transmuting

the Q4P$^\infty$ transformation from Pure Metaphysical > Hybrid

the underlying logic for the hypothesis

Pure Metaphysical   >   Hybrid Metaphysical-Physical:
(pre-Big Bang)   (post-Big Bang)
Intangible   tangible (our universe)

Once
a) one accepts as a *working hypothesis* the Big Bang theory
   (the crucial corroborating [background radiation] evidence came in 1964)
b) and considers a core premise of Potentialism Theory (see Summa III [2014])
   that Q4P$^\infty$ ignited the Big Bang
c) and notes that *life* began proximate to the formation of the Earth
d) and considers Potentialism's premise that Dark Energy and Dark Matter are
   (direct) derivatives of Q4P$^\infty$
e) and notes how Dark Energy and Dark Matter are the preponderance of the
   universe
f) and notes our ever-expanding and now accelerating universe
g) and notes the various (extraordinarily improbable) *twists and turns* that the
   universe seems to have taken enroute to *life* - and in sustaining *life* - *on earth*
   to this day,
h) and notes the related extraordinary fine-tuning of the many, many constants
   necessary for *life* on earth
i) and notes how the very laws of physics may have been altered over the eons
j) and considers that Q4P$^\infty$ is the *catalyst and driver - and complexifier* - of the
   universe

THEN

(k) it is not a super-leap to hypothesize -

that our universe was/is the *'incarnation of choice'* for formerly 100%
   metaphysical Q4P$^\infty$

that the core underlying dynamic was seeking a platform - a more versatile and powerful hybrid metaphysical-physical *platform* - from which to launch/sustain/develop (physical) life - and direct the next levels of Complexification enroute to Extraordinariation.

that Q4P∞ was compelled to *morph* for the purpose (just-noted)

that the formerly purely metaphysical core dynamic (Q4P∞) *transmuted* via the Big Bang into a hybrid metyaphysical/physical entity - our universe.

as Working Hypothesis

Potentialism Theory is proposed as a Working Hypothesis for the academic community to be dissected and challenged.

The theory works elegantly - from 'Eternal Origins' to the present moment in time

All other known cosmologies heretofore typically break down at multiple key points, including *Eternal Origins*.

Potentialism Theory is proven inductively
See Inductive1000.com
  and, also -
  Deductive1000

the Good News......is that 99% probability the theory is correct
the Bad News........is that all the textbooks will need to be changed -
    across ALL the sciences - hard & soft -
    as there is now a new 'platform'
    And, you know, *change the platform - and you 'change the entire game'*

see also: UnifyingConcept.com

Major1000.com

POTENTIALISM		RANDOMNESS
Directional		Non-directional
Challenger		Insider
Birnbaum		identity-masked clique
Transparent		in-hiding
Cosmic Prime Mover	v	no Driver
Universalistic		hard-line Atheistic
Quest for Potential		Aimlessness
American		British
1988		1859
NY		~London area

3 February 2014

THE HUFFINGTON POST

UNITED KINGDOM

Sandra Miller

Two schemas of the Universe

Current Academe is heavily under the sway of a group of academics aligned with what is often referred to as the 'entrenched orthodoxy' schema. This schema's mantra is that the universe is barren and random; its advocates are often atheistic. These advocates, whose geographic center of gravity is at seven leading colleges in southern England, often informally act in tandem, and are often referred to as advocates of Randomness/atheism. As noted, the group propounds that everything is random happenstance and chance. In turn, they assert that mankind is inconsequential in the grand scheme of things, being but a cosmic accident of no significance and importance. To this group, mankind is but an insignificant speck in a cold, random and aimless universe. The group rejects any possibility whatsoever of any transcending force or dynamic or design or spirituality or purpose in the universe. To them the universe is barren. If there is any common denominator to the universe, they would single out 'decay'. And as far as the billions of extraordinary galaxies, each with billions of extraordinary stars and assorted planetary systems, at least one of which with a quite extraordinary multitude of breathtaking organic bio-forms, well, to them it is just a random event. It all sort of 'just happened.'

A January 2014 feature article by David Gelernter, professor of computer science at Yale, "The Closing of the Scientific Mind" in *Commentary Magazine*, puts the scientific and academic community in their place on several inter-related fronts. Gelernter chastises the scientific community for what he terms 'roboticism, that is, for belittling the role of the aesthetic, the humanistic, and the spiritual. He also criticizes the scientific community at large for being too 'mechanistic,' for viewing life entities as if they were pseudo-computers with assorted binary switches.

Wrapping all these inter-related issues together, Gelernter cites the case of NYU Professor of Philosophy Thomas Nagel. In 2012 Oxford University Press published Nagel's work *Mind and Cosmos*. The thesis of the work is relatively simple: Contemporary Evolutionary Biology theory (aka 'the entrenched orthodoxy') does not 'handle' the emergence of consciousness. Nagel, like Gelernter, wants our theory of the cosmic order and its sub-theory of evolution to be richer and to account for human spirit, consciousness and subjectivity. Thus, Nagel feels that there must be a cosmic dynamic driving the universe and evolution forward in a direction which leads to consciousness. He feels that the prevailing orthodoxy, focused only on genetic survival as the sole dynamic in a universe driven only by randomness, is 'missing the boat' on what is truly happening here. In technical terms Nagel is proposing that there is a 'teleology' (a purpose 'driver' of the universe) embedded in the cosmic order.

However, in questioning the entrenched orthodoxy's failure to explain the emergence of consciousness, Nagel is but a 'schoolboy' compared to conceptual theorist and metaphysics specialist David Birnbaum. Nagel suggested in 2012 that there must be a core cosmic 'drive,' a teleology. But a major teleology (adroitly handling consciousness in-the-mix) was already published (1988, 2005) by a fellow New Yorker. Nagel's midtown Manhattan neighbor, 40 blocks north of Nagel at NYU, is David Birnbaum, author of the iconic 2-part philosophical treatise *Summa Metaphysica*. Birnbaum's work proposes an overarching cosmic dynamic: Infinite Potential. In November 2013 British journalist Oliver Burkeman, echoed French anthropologist Claude Levi-Strauss (2006) on Birnbaum's Potentialism, and called Birnbaum's theory 'remarkable and profound'; Burkeman felt that both leaders – Birnbaum and Nagel – were nicely in-sync.

Infinite Potential is the centerpiece theme of Birnbaum's proposed original overarching theory of the cosmic order, the Theory of Potential. Birnbaum's universe is organic, overflowing with potential. Indeed Potential defines it. If Nagel's work gives the 'entrenched orthodoxy' academics heartburn, then Birnbaum work gives them a massive heart attack. The Birnbaum treatise was published in two parts: *Summa Metaphysica I: God & Evil* (by Ktav Publishing in1988) and *Summa Metaphysica II: God and Good* (by New Paradigm Matrix in 2005).

Birnbaum's *Summa*, which has over fifty thousand sets in circulation, is actually in full philosophical alignment with Nagel's later Mind & Cosmos book (2012) and with Gelernter's above-noted major *Commentary* article (2014). All their works, so to speak, 'talk to each other'.

Birnbaum's Theory of Potential offers a unified, grand and dynamic cosmic construct. Birnbaum is quite aware, as we all are, that there is no shortage of seemingly 'open space' in the cosmos. However he suggests not missing the core thrust and embedded potentiality of the cosmic order.

Birnbaum proposes that his signature theme, Infinite Potential, is the eternal and ongoing dynamic of the quite rich cosmic order. What has unfolded over the ages, according to Birnbaum, is far from randomness acting out in a barren universe. "You and I, according to this theory, are individual cosmic potentials, the end-result of many billions of years of ongoing iteration and optimization. In turn, individually, we each set the stage for more potential" says Birnbaum.

There is thus a direct sequence of contemporary protagonists of a so to speak 'organic' universe: Birnbaum (1988, 2005) > Nagel (2012) > Gelernter (2014). Nagel in his 2012 work articulated that we should seek to discern the cosmic drive which brought us to life, consciousness, reason, knowledge, language and altruism. It turns out that all of the items on both the Nagel and Gelernter checklists are fully encompassed by Birnbaum's Theory of Potential. According to Potentialism, the cosmos is organic, not barren. It inexorably quests after its manifold and quite often extraordinary potentials. It seeks the full flowering of its own possibilities. This unstoppable quest for extreme potential drives our quite extraordinary and quite rich universe.

18
qeustions/conundrums
and
$Q4P^\infty \rightarrow C+ \rightarrow E+$

Simultaneous Solution!
to 18 core and key
inter-related classic questions/conundrums
In cosmology / metaphysics / philosophy
- with the one proposed dynamic

the 18 points:
What ignited our universe?
What sustains it?
What propels it forward?

From whence life?
What really drives Evolution forward?
From whence consciousness?

Is there a dynamic transcending time and space?
Is the universe fine-tuned?
Is there design to the universe?

Is there direction to our universe?
Is there a universe-goal?
Is there human purpose?

What/who is the designer?
Is there a higher force?
What is this higher force?

Why does entropy not implode the universe?
What breathes life into the equations?
What defines our universe?

the concise simultaneous solution - to all 18 above:

Infinite Quest for Potential (Q4P)
seeks Complexification (C+) enroute to Extraordination (E+).

Sounds pretty elegant to us...

Birnbaum-Super-Formula

Simultaneous

When we were in 6th, 7th grade math, it soon became apparent to us that if a potential solution seemed to resolve two problems simultaneously, it was inevitably the correct solution (to both).

In our case here, we have a concise proposed solution seeming to resolve, perhaps even 18+ overlapping problems simultaneously....

Classic Issues Aligned

POTENTIALISM THEORY

THE SUMMA METAPHYSICA SERIES

a unified

(consistent, overarching, fully integrated)

conceptual line of attack

metaphysics
cosmology
philosophy

aligning

eternal origins
Life Force
direction/teleology/driver
purpose/meaning
evolutionary theory
universe horizon

via
one Common Denominator
dynamic*

- with **theogony** and **theodicy** *in the mix* from a Religious perspective, and, *loosely defined*, still in the mix from a Spiritual or Secular perspective

* Q4P → C+ → E+

MORPHED COSMIC ORDER

Section F

MORPHED COSMIC ORDER

the end-goal of the universe-drive

POTENTIALISM THEORY

E+ Extrardinariation

---

for context
Outlier Birnbaum's Potentialism -
a metaphysics theory

$Q4P\infty \rightarrow C+ \rightarrow E+$

POTENTIALISM THEORY

wraps-around
- and complements -
iconic Einstein's Relativity -
macro-physics theory

$E = mc^2$

see Einstein1000.com

Q4P$^\infty$ and Life Force...

POTENTIALISM THEORY

... are inextricably intertwined

SUMMA SETS-THE-STAGE
1988, 2005

POTENTIALISM THEORY

FOR LLOYD's 'UNIVERSE COMPUTER'
2006

---

an elegant, consistent & unified theory

POTENTIALISM THEORY

with a supple spinal column - Q4P$^\infty$ -
coursing thru its entirety

MORPHED COSMIC ORDER

a proposed Framing Concept of the universe

the two key websites

primary:

www.SummaMetaphysica.com

secondary:

www.PotentialismTheory.com
(primarily multi-lingual translations of a selection of articles on Summa)

THE UNIVERSITY OF
MAINE
1865

" A UNIFYING CONCEPT OF THE UNIVERSE"

" David Birnbaum's *Summa Metaphysica* is a major philosophical contribution
to the study of Being. According to Summa, Holy Potential is at the very epicenter
of the Divine, and the quest for its fulfillment is the underlying core dynamic of
the cosmic order.

Birnbaum considers Quest for Potential$^\infty$ to be ubiquitous and overarching
holy cosmic dynamic. All of the countless components of the Universe,
including humans, are striving towards the full realization of their particular
potentialities.

Although centered on the problem of evil existing in the world created
by benevolent and omnipotent God, Summa reaches far beyond theodicy.
Deeply rooted in Biblical tradition, yet providing a modern and original
approach to answering millennia-old questions, *Summa* represents a bold
attempt to formulate a unifying concept of the Universe."

****

ECOLOGY

The very basic laws of ecology describing the growth and regulation of populations of living organisms appear to fit the metaphysical model of the cosmic Quest for Potential[∞] proposed by David Birnbaum. Obviously, ecology is only one of many sub disciplines within the rather broad science of biology, and biology is only one of many natural sciences (albeit a very important one). Therefore, this observation alone does not serve as an immediate and decisive proof that the Quest is indeed the major driving force behind each and every natural process.

Nevertheless, it is truly fascinating that an established scientific theory based on experimental evidence and mathematic models is in such a strong agreement with a philosophical theory of Conceptual Theorist Birnbaum, and developed independently of any formal natural history research. This is unlikely to happen by chance alone.

Therefore, it is reasonable to propose the Quest for Potential[∞] as a *working hypothesis* for explaining the impetus behind the cosmic dynamic.

Testing this hypothesis would involve a critical review of other scientific theories explaining particular phenomena in chemistry, physics, sociology, etc. for their agreement with Birnbaum's proposed Overarching Theory.

Ultimately, this may yield a unified view of the Universe, which would be a major leap in fulfilling our potentiality as conscious beings.

– Dr. Andrei Alyokhin
Professor and Graduate Coordinator
School of Biology and Ecology
University of Maine
Orono, ME
November 2, 2012
Andrei_Alyokhin@umit.maine.edu

Q4P[∞] = Survival (Potential array (Extraordinariation

Glossary

(abridged)

...of first tier of Potentialism Terms

Over the past three decades (since KTAV published Summa I in 1988) Birnbaum's Potentialism Theory has been built-out. As such, it has developed its own lexicon to describe its fundamental principle of Potentialism.

Potentialists define the universal drive of cosmology as the Infinite Quest for Potential. This is the inherent "drive" of the cosmos to seek its own ever-further complexity/sophistication/wondrousness.

Potential journeys towards a non-concretized state of infinite complexity/sophistication/wondrousness. The universe moves inexorably towards this infinite goal.

Potentialism

Potentialism itself represents a new metaphysics/science for a new century. It provides an overarching 21st century metaphysics that seeks no less than to encompass the scientific, the religious, the spiritual, the secular and the philosophical.

Fully encompassing all modern science, Potentialism is potentially (repeat: potentially) a candidate - in due course - for a (true) Theory of Everything – not only in scientific terms, but in all terms meaningful to humankind.

Potentialism seeks to arm those seeking an understanding of the cosmic order with the tools necessary to have a "seat at the table" for this new metaphysics. All are invited as science comes back to the metaphysics table after a *de facto* three century, post-Spinoza hiatus.

Following is an (abridged) short glossary of core, key terms of Potentialism.

Q4P$^\infty$ The Infinite Quest for Infinite Potential
- usually shortened to Quest for Potential in conversation, though the formal name best represents the iterative, infinite nature of Potential. This represents the universe's innate drive towards fulfilling its true potential. Also commonly denoted as Q4P$^\infty$ or, super-shorthand: Q4P.

Note that there are multiple embedded infinities in Q4P$^\infty$:
See Infinity-3.com

CWP
Cosmic Womb of Potential

C+ Complexification
The hypothesized cosmic intermediate drive – "Q4P's handmaiden" – maneuvering the cosmos towards greater complexity/sophistication/richness/integration/variety/wondrousness.

In turn, note that one of the components of Complexification just-noted above is 'integration'; meaning, Complexification does not occur divorced from the cosmic landscape; rather, Complexification integrates into-the-process the harmonization/optimization of the ongoing Complexification with the existing bio-landscape.

Complexification seeks quantum jumps – QJs (see entry in this same Glossary) – as opposed to incremental advance.

In its ongoing march of Complexification – the universe moves ever-and-ever closer to what Birnbaum calls Extraordinariation (E+) – the universal end-goal – a horizon to be approached, but never quite realized – and a state otherwise defined as hyper-Complexification.

E+ Extraordinariation.
The end-target of this journey towards increased complexity/sophistication/wondrousness is referred to as Extraordinariation (see Extraordinariation.com). Extraordinariation is not so much a precise destination as an *ideal goal* to be sought-after, albeit never quite fully-realized.

Note that Q4P itself does not quite know precisely what E+ looks like. Q4P is so *to speak* 'finding its way'. Along these lines, the Cambrian Explosion may have been a re-set.

$Q4P^\infty \rightarrow C+ \rightarrow E+$
[the SuperLaw / Super-Formula]
The fundamental, core/primal drive of the cosmic dynamic. This represents the Infinite Quest for Potential which drives the cosmic order towards greater and greater complexity and onward towards Extraordinariation.

Q4P/Q3
The fusion of -

Q4P = Infinite Quest for Potential
and
Q3 = Quantum - information processing / computing / engineering

yields >

Q4P/Q3

- the hybrid potential driver

And, it is Q4P/Q3 which tweaks the genomes
... and yields Evolution

Universe Horizon
The denouement of the universe as far out as we can project our infinitely expanding universe

*

Summa Metaphysica is a paradigm-changing work; it entirely changes the way we look at *everything*.

- M.D.

Potentialism Theory = Summa Theory = Birnbaum Theory = Q4P Theory = Quantum Man Theory

the eternal

metaphysical spinal column, life force, *Chi*

of the Cosmic Order

Albert Einstein, in his book *The World As I See It*, stated that the harmony of natural law "reveals an intelligence of such superiority that, compared with it, all the systematic thinking and acting of human beings is an utterly insignificant reflection."

$Q4P^{\infty}$ = the Cosmic Instinct

POTENTIALISM THEORY

**encapsulation formula
of our universe**

$$Q4P^{\infty} \rightarrow C+ \rightarrow E+$$

In a letter to a child who asked if scientists pray, Einstein wrote, "Everyone who is seriously involved in the pursuit of science becomes convinced that a spirit is manifest in the laws of the Universe – a spirit vastly superior to that of man, and one in the face of which we with our modest powers must feel humble."

hitherto undiscerned

**Potentialism Theory posits that there exists
a hitherto undiscerned core and transcendent dynamic**

$Q4P^{\infty}$

aka

Quest for Potential$^{\infty}$

**which not only drives the universe,
but actually IS the universe.**

*

**We are all fully integral to this dynamic -
as hard as that proposition might be.**

MORPHED COSMIC ORDER

multi-tasker

Summa develops the themes
that this proposed formula
$$Q4P^{\infty} \rightarrow C+ \rightarrow E+$$
is simultaneously:

    (a) a dynamic
    (b) a description *of a process*,
    (c) the direction of the universe
    (d) the teleology / purpose / 'driver' - of the universe
    (e) a concise formula encapsuling *the entire universe*
    (f) possibly the formula for '*life force*'
    (g) the metaphysical/spiritual arc of the Cosmic Order

more amplification below

Push-Pull

Aristotelian metaphysics is Push.

The Prime Mover (Latin: *primum movens*) drives the universe forward.

Potentialism Theory, however, is Push-Pull

Potential both pushes forward and pulls forward (beckons forth).

Like labor at childbirth, which mimics cosmic dynamics, Potentialism Theory metaphysics is Push-Pull.

The potential of a system - large or small - ever-so-subtly opens a potential pathway for the system.

Q4P∞- directed Evolution

Evolution is not directed by
Natural Selection / Random Mutation
(the fatally-flawed Darwinian theory)

Evolution is hyper-intelligently designed
by Q4P∞ - a secular dynamic
primed as-its-essence
to build-out Complexification (C+)
enroute to Extraordinariation (E+)

There is, thus, respectfully,
a powerful secular resolution path to resolving/understanding
the extraordinarily intelligently-crafted
hyper-complex and ongoing journey of Evolution

The hitherto intractable scientific conundrum of Evolution
is elegantly resolved (by Potentialism Theory)
without deploying concepts of Creator-designed Evolution

'Complexification Evolution'

Potentialism Theory rejects both
(a) Creationism and (b) Natural Selection

Rather, species have (ensemble) inexorably evolved through
my hypothesized
"Complexification Evolution",

This ever-unfolding dynamic
vectors towards Extraordinariation+
by my hypothesized (secular)
(evolving Quantum Mechanics-based)
Quest for Potential$^\infty$, (Q4P$^\infty$)

(with Q4P$^\infty$ being
the hitherto undiscerned and underlying
primal & ~eternal
cosmic force/dynamic).

The track of 'Complexification Evolution'
inexorably follows my hypothesized SuperLaw,
$$Q4P^\infty \rightarrow C+ \rightarrow E+$$

Simultaneously, on a personal level, I believe that our (secular) universe of Potential itself quests
after (elusive) God and Spirituality -
as components of its inexorable march towards Extraordinariation -
under the umbrella of the same above-noted hypothesized SuperLaw:

Hyper-Intelligent Design

\# Evolution is, indeed, driven by hyper-intelligent design

\# The designer/iterator is (secular) **Q4P**$^\infty$

\# (asserted) Natural Selection / Random Mutation is a non-starter

\# No need to deploy the biblical **'Creator'** here

\# **Q4P**$^\infty$ re-configures genes and designs new ones;
   The 'designer' does not re-purpose mutations

Dissent against Conventional Wisdom

"The scientist must be free to answer any question,
to doubt any assertion, to seek for any evidence,
to correct any errors."

- Physicist J. Robert Oppenheimer

Potentialism Theory = Summa Theory = Birnbaum Theory = Q4P Theory = Quantum Man Theory

the quantum physics to backstop Summa Theory

a Birnbaum hypothesis

Birnbaum:Lloyd

see also 2006 *Programming the Universe* by Seth Lloyd
Professor of Mechanical Engineering & Physics at MIT

This (2006) seminal Lloyd work came out after Summa I (November, 1988)
and Summa II (March, 2005). - and prior to Summa III (2014).

Professor Seth Lloyd - from stellar MIT - furnishes a (timely ;) crucial -
and hitherto missing - breakthrough
***cutting-edge science nuts & bolts mechanics / quantum physics
mechanism***
to backstop the metaphysics of Summa Theory.

translation: 'Insider' Lloyd of MIT ensures (in 2006) that 'outlier' Birnbaum's
proposed (1988, 2005, 2014) global and over-arching (macro-micro)
paradigm shift will prevail.

(more on Lloyd:Birnbaum further down)

the quantum physics to backstop Summa Theory (continued)

a Birnbaum hypothesis

Birnbaum:Lloyd

Paralleling Birnbaum

Lloyd (2006-2007) presents a
Quantum Mechanics theory
of a **Quantum Computer** universe

paralleling

Birnbaum's (1988 + 2005)
orinigal/breakthrough
Conceptual Metaphysical theory
of a **Q4P∞ (Quest for Potential)** universe

the key contemporary
scientific hypothesis **bridge** to Summa

**from a secular / scientific / mechanistic perspective -

"All interactions between particles in the universe...convey not only energy but also information in other words, particles not only collide, they
compute. What is the entire universe computing, ultimately? Its own
dynamical evolution... As the computation proceeds, reality unfolds."

-from the back-cover of *Programming the Universe*
By Seth Lloyd, Professor, Mechanical Engineering, MIT
(c) 2006, First Vintage Books Edition (NY)

Lloyd's hypothesis provides key **1:1 buttress** to Summa.

Indeed, "**Q4P∞ is hiding in plain sight**," - both conceptually and literally -
as we have hypothesized since 1988 via *Summa Metaphysica* I (hardcover),
and then via *Summa Metaphysica* II (2005 online, 2008 softcover)

Birnbaum's **Q4P∞**
resonates as a fuller multi-dimensional
wrap-around conceptualization re:
Lloyd's **universe as a programming entity**

*MIT scientist Seth Lloyd directs the Center for Extreme
Quantum Information Theory at MIT, where he is also a
professor of Mechanical Engineering.

**excerpt, not a testimonial

Both Birnbaum's Q4P∞ (Quest for Potential∞) dynamic and Lloyd's Quantum Computer
are (eternally) *building-out* from the eternal 'Genesis Point';
they are each ~infinitely iterating & optimizing -
drawing-from an ever-richer pool of resources;
each has, as well, essentially 'become' the universe -
advancing onwward and outward into the unknown;
the disciplines, language, lenses, and imagery may seem to diverge,
but the core dynamics - and implications of the two cosmologies - are eerily parallel.

the quantum physics to backstop Summa Theory (continued)

a Birnbaum hypothesis

Birnbaum:Lloyd

1:1 Resonance ?

Parallel to *Summa*, albeit highly mechanistic

excerpts from
PROGRAMMING THE UNIVERSE
A QUANTUM COMPUTER SCIENTIST TAKES ON THE COSMOS
Seth Lloyd

Published by Alfred A. Knopf ©2006

"The history of the universe is, in effect, a huge and ongoing
quantum computation. The universe is a quantum computer.
    This begs the question: What does the universe compute?
It computes itself. The universe computes its own behavior. As
soon as the universe began, it began computing. At first, the
patterns it produced were simple, comprising elementary particles
and establishing the fundamental laws of physics. In time, as it
processed more and more information, the universe spun out ever
more intricate and complex patterns, including galaxies, stars, and
planets. Life, language, human beings, society, culture—all owe
their existence to the intrinsic ability of matter and energy to process
information. The computational capability of the universe explains
one of the great mysteries of nature: how complex systems such as

living creatures can arise from fundamentally simple physical laws....
(p. 3)

The digital revolution under way today is merely the latest in
a long line of information-processing revolutions stretching back
through the development of language, the evolution of sex, and
the creation of life, to the beginning of the universe itself. Each
revolution has laid the ground-work for the next...." (p. 5)

Lloyd directs the Center for Extreme Quantum Information Theory (xQIT) at
MIT.

so,
Metaphysical/Holistic Birnbaum's Quest for Potential (Q4P∞)
has 1:1 resonance with
neo-Mechanstic Lloyd's 'universe computer'

Conceptually, one schema reinforces the other -
as both 'unities' are all-embracing, all-universe, all-encompassing,
ongoing-iterating, and inexorably-advancing.

So,
put another way....
per Birnbaum's Potentialism Theory,
via the quantum,
(see quantum mechanic maestro Lloyd for the nuts & bolts)
our supra-organic and fully-integrated universe
optimizes, then iterates
- in an ongoing loop -
on every level (macro thru micro)
and integrates
across the entire universe (ongoing),
factoring-in short, medium and long term.

[Meaning, Q4P is a 'busy boy']

- DB

On Cosmology, Evolution
per Lloyd*

"In fact, the chance of an ordered universe like ours arising out of random flips of a coin is so small as to be effectively zero." - p. 57

"The amount of information in a gene can be measured; the human genome possesses some 6 billion bits of information." - p. 15

*Lloyd, *Programming the Universe*, Knopf, 2007, NY.

our 'Smart Universe' driven by our hypothesized *natural force* (Q4P)

REAL

We are as real as always.

It is just that our core gene sequence -
which was arrived at 200,000 years-ago when the modern form of humans evolved -
is a result of Q4P∞ tweaking the genome (per Potentialism Theory); and not as a result of Natural Selection / Random Mutation (per Darwinism Theory);
or of pure chance.

The Creation of of a New Species

- is a highly-sophisticated operation/endeavor

Multiply that sophisticated work by several billion species

It is a serious undertaking - for a -

hyper-intelligent / hyper-powerful / hyper-focused
SOMETHING *

We identify that SOMETHING as Q4P∞

And our position is that -

> No species has ever been created by
> (ultimately fatally-flawed)
> Natural Selection / Random Mutation (*aka* Darwinism) -
> and none ever will be

The Darwin clan can surreptitiously shovel mllions of British Sterling
directly - and indirectly -
into *undermining* other theories and theorists -
but their gambit will prove futile - because the Darwin theory is -
after all is said and done - dead wrong. **

And, now, rumor has it that
there is a new kid on the block - with a real theory -
which elegantly works.-
on all levels - in all time periods ***

* this proposition is the polar-opposite of Natural Selection-Random Mutation aka
Darwinism

** see Evolution1000.com

*** future generations looking at all this will emote -
as regards Darwinism - *What were they thinking?*

MORPHED COSMIC ORDER

Section G

MORPHED COSMIC ORDER

our purpose-driven universe

POTENTIALISM THEORY

[Extraordinariation, that is]

"Remarkable and profound"

POTENTIALISM THEORY

- Claude Levi-Strauss, Paris

BIRNBAUMIAN EVOLUTION

POTENTIALISM THEORY

Evolution1000.com

Q4P$^\infty$ is pervasive across the universe

POTENTIALISM THEORY

its salient manifestation is Dark Energy -
a derivative of Q4P$^\infty$

Directional Universe

POTENTIALISM THEORY

Direction1000.com

Science has been averse
to looking behind the veil of the Big Bang;

POTENTIALISM THEORY

nevertheless, Potentialism Theory hypothesizes/delineates
two distinct EPOCHS behind the veil
(of the Big Bang)

MORPHED COSMIC ORDER

Fusion Evolution

Metaphysical / Quantum

- Birnbaum, *Summa Metaphysica III*, January, 2014

Potentialism Evolution

Evolution

Quest for Potential / Quantum Mechanics

Q4P/Q3

tweaks the genomes (ensemble)

the Birnbaum Evolution hypothesis

Potentialism Evolution

Summa's Metaphysics fused with Lloyd's Quantum Mechanics

Evolution / panel A

Evolution: the next focus of Potentialism Theory

Darwinism is fatally flawed

\# The entire Natural Selection / Random Mutations proposition (aka Darwinism) is fatally flawed.

\# Respectfully, notwithstanding its global standing, Natural Selection / Random Mutation simply does not advance the Evolution drama.

\# The confluence of factors which launched and sustained the theory at the very center of academe is a bizarre 150+ year saga worthy of examination; but that saga is not the focus.

a1) Except in Marvel (superhero) comic books, mutations are typically weaker than the original;
a positive mutation is rare, at best; this reality is not a formula for dynamic evolution.

a2) Intergral to DNA - the foundation of life - is (*ultra highly sophisticated* and complex) sequenced digital coding; even one random mutation of this sophisticated coding does not end well; mutations undermine 'the foundation of life'; mutations do not enhance life. Compound mutations of this coding are disastrous, not salutary, for the potential of the life form.

a3) At least three dozen *universal constants are ultra highly fine-tuned* for the existence of life; were these constants truly fine-tuned by random mutation? Seriously?

b) Even if the Darwinian concept were, in principle, viable, one key challenge is that one would still need "a trillion-trillion times" the time (4.0-4.5 billion years) currently allotted for the 5 billion new species.

In the human genome there are 3 billion nucleotides
(and corresponding 3 billion characters of digital code)

The odds against having gotten to this sequence randomly are
greater than 26 to the power of 3 billion........
Would you take these odds?

Respectfully, classic and well-established Probability Theory would reject random
mutation generating five billion species over 4-4.5 billion years as a *viable denouement*.
Probability Theory can be deployed for *possibility*, not for *de facto* impossibility*. [To
argue to the contrary - per the mainstream consensus - is, respectfully, simply *group-
think* run amok.]

As in cosmology, randomness is clearly amply present on-stage in Evolution, but, once
again, is not a component in evolution.

c1) SPECIES: The Cambrian explosion was just half billion year ago. With its uniquely rich
and extraordinary multitude of new species - within a super-narrow ~19 million year
slice of time**, it belies Darwinism.
This issue alone is fatal to Darwinian (Natural Selection / Random Mutation) Theory.

c2) PHYLA: All the major phyla seem to have appeared during the Cambrian Explosion
(maximum currently guestimated duration: a very narrow 30 million years).

Thirty million years is a very narrow sliver of the 4.5 billion years of our earth;
thus, just by the paragraph above, Darwinian Natural Selection / Random Mutation
is clearly simply not a significant factor in advanced Evolution.

d) How could complex *bio-chemical transformations*
possibly result from the proposed randomness Darwinian mechanism?
Per Michael Boehe's presentations, biological systems at the molecular level
present hyper-complexity even greater than complexity at other levels.

e) How does one get *biological creativity/innovation/super-complexity* -
from linear, spaced-out mutations?

f) How does Darwinism explain - *"linearly irreducible complexity"*
(my term / I expanded the classic 'irreducible complexity' term)
i.e. *complexity instances* in organisms which simply could not have occurred via a linear
mutation-sequence *stretched-out* over time (per standard Darwinian prognostication).
See also discussions by Michael Boehe - including on YouTube -
debunking the alleged 'science' here.

g) The *fossil* record in general and pre-Cambrian, in particular, does not jibe
with Darwinian theory (see also David Berlinski discussions).

h) Per Randomness / Darwinism - where did
 - *first life*
 - *the first cell*
 and
 - *the first species*

each come from?

No answer, Darwinian crew?

Not one species will ever be birthed via Darwinism, let alone billions of species,
even if a trillion years were allotted for even one new species.

Evolution is achieved by Q4P∞ introducing new genes; by re-wiring gene networks;
and by deliberate and complex
sequenced bio-chemical transformations choreographed by Q4P∞;
Evolution is not achieved via mutations;
not via a slo-mo and simplistic stretched-out linear sequence of random mutations.
In-the-mix, new proteins and concomitant digital coding must be introduced.
And just where is this new digital coding coming from?
It is certainly not coming from random mutation;
rather, the new (digital) coding is coming to you courtesy of digital-based Q4P∞.

----

*See Lloyd, *Programming the Universe*, Knopf, 2007, NY, p. 57

"In fact, the chance of an ordered universe like ours arising out of random flips of a coin is
so small as to be effectively zero."

** 19 million years Cambrian period - out of, say, 4.5 billion years = 4/10 of 1% of the total
time sequence....yielding well over 50% of the most complex/sophisticated species?
[Meaning, *insufficient time* for Natural Selection / Random Mutation
to produce billions of super-complex species.]
Why is that theory (Darwinism) still afloat at all?
As the expression goes, "*What are they smoking?*"

the Birnbaum Evolution hypothesis

Potentialism Evolution

Summa's Metaphysics fused with Lloyd's Quantum Mechanics

Evolution / panel B

reminder:
Q4P encompasses the fusion of -
Quantum-information processing + Quantum-computing + Quantum-engineering
to play-out
Q4P → C+ → E+

Q4P re-engineering the genomes

Other Related Theorists

What Charles Darwin (On the Origin of Species 1859) reads as 'natural selection';

what George C. Williams (Adaptation and Natural Selection, 1966)
and Richard Dawkins (The Selfish Gene 1976)
are reading as 'gene-centered Evolution';

what Murray Gell-Man (The Quark and the Jaguar 1994) is viewing as 'complex adaptive systems'

what Stuart Kauffman (At Home in the Universe 1995) is reading as 'self-organizing systems';

what David Pines (Complex Adaptive Matter 2005) is reading as 'complex adaptive matter',

are all actually *one and the same*:

the Potentialim Evolution hypothesis -

What they are viewing, is actually **Q4P re-engineering the genomes**

More technically, they are (typically) viewing Q4P on a local-level/micro-level tweaking & re-engineering an individual genome.

However, the plot thickens....

Q4P Evolution is operating simultaneously in an integrated fashion across all the genomes of our planet

Meaning, the *educated hypothesis* is that plant genomes will be *re-engineering* ensemble with human genomes and ensemble with insect genomes, *etc.*

Why the integrated choreography? Because, of course, all the 'pieces' need to advance (and fit/interact) together *ensemble* / efficiently / dynamically - on the C+ march towards E+.

*

Woese

note: the now-established phenomenon (per Carl R. Woese d. 2012) of H.G.T (Horizontal Gene Transfer) - that DNA itself can indeed move sideways, across barriers, from one kind of creature to another - would buttress (Summa's) Evolution Theory above.

Summa (just above) posits simultaneous (varied) re-engineering across 'barriers' (life forms); Woese (in the late 1990s) posited simultaneous identical DNA-cluster replicating across 'barriers'. So, Woese was on a parallel but different track. [However, I suspect that Woese may have missed important variations in the 'replications' - and, in fact, was observing *precisely* what I am hypothesizing.]

Some macro Observations

Five billion (ever more sophisticated and wondrous) species over the lifespan course of *life* on our planet.

Random mutations **crucially** *setting the stage* for the inexorable advance/expansion and Complexification of the species on our planet?
No, the random mutations are an insignificant *side show*, not factoring-into evolution

So, Evolution, YES; but the catalyst and driver is Q4P.

Notwithstanding the politically correct pro-Darwinian view, random genetic mutations in nature are (per Potentialism Theory) respectfully simply not a factor in evolutionary biology. And, yes, correct, Natural Selection, a pillar of modern biology, falls. The 1-2 punch of iconic Darwinism - Natural Selection / Random Mutation , however established in modern science, is fatally-flawed.

["Common Ancestor" aka "Common Descent", another legacy of Darwin, is not addressed by Potentialism Theory directly.]

In both cosmology, in general, and evolution, in particular, Q4P is 'cracking the whip' and 'running the show'; not Randomness.

Both cosmology and related evolutionary biology are 'directional', not random-chance.

In both cases, we do not ride a multi-billion year trajectory towards E+ (Extraordinariation) via randomness. It is hard enough for ('directional') metaphysical/quantum hyper-intelligence Q4P to pull this off ;)

Building-out the Cosmic Order - ongoing over the eons - requires a (directional) hyper-intelligent prime prime time catalyst - $Q4P^{\infty}$.

the Birnbaum Evolution hypothesis

Potentialism Evolution

Summa's Metaphysics fused with Lloyd's Quantum Mechanics

Evolution / panel C

reminder:
Q4P encompasses the fusion of -
Quantum-information processing + Quantum-computing + Quantum-engineering
to play-out
$Q4P \rightarrow C+ \rightarrow E+$

TimeLine / Context

A) John Archibald Wheeler (1911-2008) sets the quantum mechanics stage
   from his Princeton base (from 1938 onwards) for Seth lloyd (1960 to the present);

B) Summa Metaphysica series 1988, 2005, 2014
   and 2020 [w-i-p Quantum Man]

C) and Seth Lloyd (from his MIT base) furnishes the quantum mechanics 'wiring' for
   Potentialism Theory

D) More specifically, Wheeler's iconic proposition of *It from Bit* (Santa Fe Institute Spring 1989) sets the stage for Lloyd's *the universe as computer* (2006: Programming the Universe).

E) As per the three panels Birnbaum:Lloyd above,
Lloyd furnishes the quantum mechanics to support the Potentialism metaphysics.

F) Lloyd's quantum mechanics (*via bits*) proposition for:
quantum - information processing / computing / engineering,
dovetails seamlessly into Potentialism's more conceptual Evolution theory.

G) Lloyd himself (as of JAN 2020) still has not extrapolated his quantum mechanics into an evolutionary theory. (He may be wary of inciting the Atheist/Randomness gang.)

Recap

	Cosmology	Evolution
Randomess formulation	*aimless/random*	*aimless/random* mutation - with survival-directional Darwinism then guiding
Potentialism theory	Directional Q4P	Directional Q4P

Thus, Randomness Formulation deploys a non-directional 'play' - *aimlessness* - somehow first to ignite our universe. and then to sustain / drive / iterate / optimize / expand
our universe - over a 14 billion year span and counting. In the mix, non-directional 'aimlessness' somehow - miraculously - allegedly via random mutations - drives Evolution forward from a single cell entity to 21st Century humans and associated consciousness. Quite a feat for an '*aimless*' play.

Potentialism, on the other hand, deploys its quite-directional core dynamic -
Q4P - across both Cosmology and Evolution.

*

[theory development: historical trajectory]

the Birnbaum Evolution hypothesis

Potentialism Evolution

Summa's Metaphysics fused with Lloyd's Quantum Mechanics

Evolution / panel D

reminder:
Q4P encompasses the fusion of -
Quantum-information processing + Quantum-computing + Quantum-engineering
to play-out
Q4P → C+ → E+

Evolution
[per Potentialism Theory]

Q4P tweaks the genomes
[theory development: historical trajectory]

c. 350 BCE (384 BCE-322 BCE)
Aristotle /
The universe has 'direction';
but that 'direction' is not known
or delineated by Aristotle

c. 1557 (1534-1572)
Baal Shem Tov / Founder, Hasidism
The entire universe is one interconnected
Life Force

c. 1677 (1632-1677)
Spinoza / *Ethics*
The universe is a *lattice-work;*
meaning, it is thoroughly inter-connected

c. 1745 (1698-1760)
Isaac Luria / founder of Modern Kabbalah
The universe emerges from the '*No End*'

1859
Darwin / *Origin of Species*
Evolution / Natural Selection

MORPHED COSMIC ORDER

1988

Birnbaum / *Summa* I Potentialism Theory
Infinite Quest for Potential (Q4P)
ignited and drives the universe;

new paradigm Potentialism Theodicy
gains global traction

Proposed eternal dynamic Infinite Quest for Potential
overthrows all classic metaphysics,
and lays the groundwork for Directional Universe

1990

John Wheeler / "It from Bit"
Information, Physics & Quantum
(Sub-atomic) information bits are the
foundation of the universe.

2005

Birnbaum / *Summa II*
Q4P drives the universe;

the Birnbaum SuperFormula:
Infinite Quest for Potential (Q4P) >
Complexification (C+) >
Extraordinariation (E+)

presentation/delineation of
Direction of the Universe

Provides an Overarching Metaphysics / Simultaneous Solution

2006

Seth Lloyd / *Programming the Universe*
Quantum Mechanics proposition:
In each atom there are bits which
communicate with bits in other atoms
across the universe - and compute the
advance/buildout of the universe ongoing

2014

'Birnbaum/Potentialism Evolution' theory - with MIT *in the mix*.

A fully-integrated secular metaphysics/cosmology

Overthrows *Randomness* across multiple fronts
(including vis à vis Cosmology and Evolution)

Creation Ex Nihilo+

David.Birnbaum.NY@gmail.com

the Birnbaum Evolution hypothesis

Potentialism Evolution

Summa's Metaphysics fused with Lloyd's Quantum Mechanics

Evolution / panel E

reminder:
Q4P encompasses the fusion of -
Quantum-information processing + Quantum-computing + Quantum-engineering
to play-out
Q4P → C+ → E+

Evolution

	Potentialism	Darwinism
Common ancestor?	N*	Y
Species evolve?	Y	Y
the literal Biblical presentation	N	N
Evolution gamut	planet-wide; inter-connected	local; not inter-connected
driven by a transcendent dynamic?	Y	N
Driver	Infinite Quest for Potential (Q4P)	Natural Selection / Random Mutations
underpinning	Quantum Mechanics	Struggle for existence

MORPHED COSMIC ORDER

Designer?	Yes / Q4P∞	No / none
Conceptualizer	David Birnbaum (Manhattan)	Charles Darwin (Kent/Greater London)
Core Text	Summa	Origin of Species 1859

* Ancestor of Man was one of the complex species progenitors
launched/created by "the designer' during the narrow
(30 million-year wide) Cambrian Explosion c. 500 mill BCE.

the Birnbaum Evolution hypothesis

Potentialism Evolution

Summa's Metaphysics fused with Lloyd's Quantum Mechanics

Evolution / panel F

reminder:
Q4P encompasses the fusion of -
Quantum-information processing + Quantum-computing + Quantum-engineering
to play-out
Q4P → C+ → E+

Intelligence

Q4P intelligence >
produced
human intelligence >
which *produced*
AI

- but each is quite distinct and unique

Potentialism Theory = Summa Theory = Birnbaum Theory = Q4P Theory = Quantum Man Theory

There are no *random universes*

POTENTIALISM THEORY

There are only Q4P$^\infty$ universes
- and maybe just one at the moment

We are not *random Mutation*

POTENTIALISM THEORY

We are Q4P-guided *Transformation*

Multiverse theory *aka* Infinite Universes theory

POTENTIALISM THEORY

still requires (directional) Q4P$^\infty$ in-the-mix
for there to be any universe whatsoever anywhere

*

Thus, Randomness Theory remains vacuous and
intellectually bankrupt

a directional universe

- Birnbaum, Summa Metaphysica II, March, 2005

Directional***
U N I V E R S E

The Birnbaum *super-formula* ALGORITHM

$$Q4P^\infty \to C+ \to E+$$

Quest for Potential$^\infty$ → Complexification → Extraordinariation

The Birnbaum-posited
Direction/Teleology/Driver
of the universe

- from Summa Metaphysica II, 2005

**WITH DIRECTIONAL UNIVERSE DEMONSTRATED HERE
TO BE SELF-EVIDENT IN COMPLEXIFICATION**

ZOOM-IN
MICRO:
the close-in focus:
the 'mechanistic driver' of the universe

C+
Complexification

First, in the **life sciences**, we now can see the trajectory from the atom to molecules to single celled organisms to multi-celled organisms to photosynthesis and plants; then as we continue to advance forward, we move into the (more complex) Animal Kingdom then onto (even more complex) humans — with ever greater and wider complexity/sophistication/wondrousness, freedom of action, brainpower, emotional array and indeed, consciousness.

Laying out the Q4P → C+ → E+ trajectory on a more macro level vis à vis the **history of the cosmos**, we now know that the trajectory post-Big Bang is very roughly as-follows: from Big Bang point > expanding universe of energy > gas Clouds > embryonic Galaxies > Stars > super-complex Galaxies and planetary systems and ever-expanding universe > embryonic Life on Earth > evolution of sex, advanced/sophisticated/complex Life forms > development of brains, language, numbers, reading, writing, computing, emailing, artificial intelligence, ever-wider spectrum emotion and ever-higher levels of consciousness - in the persons of *homo sapiens.* - a trajectory which, of couse, dovetails with the *life sciences* trajectory just delineated just-above.

Q.E.D.

ZOOM-OUT

MACRO

the broader view:

the overarching 'metaphysical driver' of the Cosmic Order

$Q4P^{\infty}$	$\rightarrow$	C+	$\rightarrow$	E+
Quest for Potential$^{\infty}$	$\rightarrow$	**Complexification**	$\rightarrow$	**Extraordinariation**

$\longrightarrow$

***Meaning,
the equation is *simultaneously* the :

\# METAPHYSICAL DIRECTION OF THE UNIVERSE
\# METAPHYSICAL DRIVER OF THE UNIVERSE
\# LIFE-FORCE/CHI OF THE UNIVERSE
\# PURPOSE/GOAL OF THE UNIVERSE
\# (entire) UNIVERSE ITSELF

ALL ARE ONE-AND-THE-SAME

- D. Birnbaum
Potentialism Theory
Summa Metapysica
1988 and onwards

some equations are more nimble than others - DB :)

Birnbaum-Super-Formula

nr = not relevant   M = Maybe

CURRENT DEBATE

The current
cosmological/metaphysical/philosophical
debate

the Theory / attributes	Creationism[9]	Intelligent Design	Darwinism / New Atheism	Potentialism / Q4P∞
Universe is Designed?	Y	Y	N	Y
Is DRIVER "alive"?	Y	~Y	N	~Y[6]
Directional / Deliberate?	Y	Y	N[2]	Y
Random?	N	N	Y	N
seeks after God?	nr[1]	?	N	M
a legislating force?	Y	?	N	N
DRIVER has, as well, classic consciousness in-the-mix	Y	?	N	N[3]
DRIVER has its own *sui generis* consciousness?	Y	?	N	Y[7]
DRIVER has classic emotion in-the-mix	Y	?	N	N[3]
Law of the Universe as core component?	N	N	N	Y[4]
Greatest good - for greatest number	Y	?	N	Y
classic spiritual force?	Y	?	N	M[3]
Is the DRIVER itself the pre-eminent Life-Force?	Y	?	N	Y
Does the DRIVER's Life Force course through our individual systems (bodies)?	N[5]	?	N	Y

the Theory / attributes	Creationism[*9]	Intelligent Design	Darwinism / New Atheism	Potentialism / Q4P∞
Did the DRIVER via the Big Bang, morph into our UNIVERSE?	N	N	N	Y
Is the DRIVER an extension of Quantum Mechanics or *vice versa?*	N	N	N	Y
Is the DRIVER/Designer hyper-intelligent?	Y[*8]	Y	N	Y[*8]

*1   IS God

*2   but a better species version will prevail

*3   Inexorably seeks VICARIOUS fuller emotion & fuller consciousness & fuller spirituality
     via humanity, in particular

*4   Q4P∞ → C+ → E+

*5   not per Jewish core doctrine;
     but God, per doctrine, is the 'Source of Life';
     and a 'spark of the Divine' is in each of us.

*6   see panel: ALIVE?
     Is the DRIVER, Q4P∞ - which gives and sustains life - and which actually defines life -
     actually "alive" ITSELF - in the sense that we are used to?

*7   [Digital? for Q4P∞]   v. [Non-Digital for humans]

*8   Hyper-Intelligent / super-BRAIN

*9   'Creationism' embraces a spectrum of beliefs regarding evolution (or non-evolution) of Man, in particular;
     but there is a common denominator core belief in a supernatural act of divine creation - of life on our
     planet - and that Man was deliberately (and carefully) 'designed' by the Divine.

an order of its own

**A revolution must aim at the destruction of the given order -
and will succeed only by asserting an order of its own.**

- RUDOLF ARNHEIM, *Entropy and Art: An Essay on Disorder and Order*

the alleged competition

Issues with the (competing) Randomness formulation

It is clearly dead-wrong
see Direction panel just-above

Internally contradictory?
The same entrenched British Randomness academic clique which fanatically defends its (non-directional) Theory of No Theory - *Randomness*, simultaneously fanatically defends (directional) Evolution.

alchemy?
Notorious alchemists swore they could turn lead into gold. However that seems like a simple trick compared to contemporary hard-line Randomnist *High Priests* who profess that their theory turns the random void into our rocking and rolling - for 14 billion years - universe.
Is the Randomness formulation simply the 'successor theory' to alchemy?

Second Law of Thermodynamics:
Why does our allegedly random universe not implode from entropy? [hint: because it is driven forward by (competing Potentialism Theory's) Q4P, and not randomly]

combination - The Emperor's Clothes and The Wizard of Oz?
Is the fantastical *Randomness* formulation not a 1:1 parallel to these just-noted fables of vacuousness?

We are all still waiting for the actual theory:
The hard-line Randomness clique has perfected the dark art of "*toxifying*" any theorist who dares disagree with their aimless and hollow construct; but, after 150+ years, for their part they have yet to produce an *actual theory*. [translation: the Randomness/Aimlessness clique is an *intellectual charlatan*]

From the shadows, the Randomnist clique hyper- aggressively mauls 'directional universe' theorists, but never actually seems to present an actual theory. Are we supposed to conflate *frenzied attacks* with an *actual theory*? To paraphrase the diss used by Texas cattlemen to characterize *big bluster / no substance* characters: These Randomness *hombres* are ALL HAT; NO CATTLE.

defining our universe:
There are many and significant random dimensions to our universe; but, *randomness* does not define it; rather, (competing Potentialism Theory's) *Quest for Potential* defines our universe.

'Randomness' Invalidated by Fine-Tuned Universe proposition
Is the universe fine-tuned for life? This proposition has gained increasing prominence and traction.

The proposition reached *critical mass* in 1999 with the publication of *Just Six Numbers* by Martin Rees, distinguished *British Astronomer Royal*. The proposition is directly *antithetical* to the Randomness proposition; the proposition *negates* Randomness. Rees went on to become head of the Royal Society.

Randomness may have been frontally challenged prior, including by Summa I, 1988, but Randomness 'is slain' by the 1999 Rees work; and a *stake is driven in its heart* by Summa II (2005).

'Defaming' is not 'Debating'
Some hard-line Randomness proponents seem confused. 'Defaming opposing theorists' - typically through paid surrogates/*hit men* - does actually *not* qualify for 'debating opposing theorists'.

Denial of Negative Reality
The first requirement of a theorist is to deal with reality. The *'denial of negative reality'* psychosis can be hazardous to one's legacy. The core tenet of Randomness - *non-directionality*, has been clearly scientifically demonstrated to be false- on two fronts: Fine-Tuned universe (see Martin Rees, *Just Six Numbers* (1999) and Direction section from David Birnbaum, *Summa Metaphysica II* (2005).

Contrary to the first - and only - axiom of Randomness, the universe, is unequivocally directional. See **Directional**.

'Game Over'?

For over a decade, and on two key different fronts, Randomness is in checkmate. Both Fine-Tuned universe formulation and the empirically demonstrated Complexification C+ / complexity teleology (universe purpose/direction) respectfully frontally render the Randomness formulation of 'no directionality' fatally undermined and disproven. The emperor, indeed, *had no clothes.*

the Randomness 'Theory of No Theory'

No theory.
No content.
No core work.
No formulation.
No science.
No cosmology.

Basics

The earth is not flat; the sun does not orbit the earth; our universe did not randomly ignite, gain traction, evolve, and steadily iterate towards ever-increasing sophistication and wondrousness ongoing for 14 billion years and counting.

intellectual 'sleight of hand" ?

There is no scientific anchoring whatsoever.
Random universe is simply *hocus pocus* masquerading as science.

product of an "echo chamber" discussion?

Group Think?

Go along to get along?

Bandwagon syndrome?

more akin to the mantra of a medieval nihilistic cult

- than to a serious academic discussion in 21st Century England

a fanatic - and in-vain - gambit

- to align science with **hard-line Atheism** (*de facto* a fundamentalist and militant anti-directional universe belief system).

"Big Brother" modus operandi

No debate; No discussion; No competition of ideas.

The Last Trophy

Darwinism is "the last trophy" of the former British Empire

And, *the-rumor-is*

that to preserve that last trophy

'the Empire' - and its 'stellar British acolytes' -

have *gang-like* bullied the Western academic world

- and stifled academic advance -

via a trans-Atlantic racketeering-like *modus operandi*

[poisonous negative branding, academic blackmail, toxic
planted articles, jarring character assassination - *and the like*]

for well-over 100 years

- and, for sure, ongoing currently in full-throttle abuse-mode
     'The so-fancy Empire' -

- ongoing in felonious *thug-mode*

Of course, only a rumor

Newton would weep

MORPHED COSMIC ORDER

New Paradigm Matrix™

21st CENTURY PUBLISHING
150+ AUTHORS/SCHOLARS

Section H

MORPHED COSMIC ORDER

"Birnbaum's approach is essentially that of the intellectual, philosopher, theologian"

POTENTIALISM THEORY

- Canadian Catholic Review
juxtaposing Weisel v. Birnbaum

Q4P$^\infty$ is the *fount of life*

POTENTIALISM THEORY

Q4P$^\infty$ courses through our blood - in force

THREE EPOCHS

POTENTIALISM THEORY

CHRONOLOGY1000.COM

a unified metaphysics

POTENTIALISM THEORY

by *outlier* David Birnbaum
Harvard University '74

'Cracks the Cosmic Code'

POTENTIALISM THEORY

- Huffington Post review headline - 6/10/15

for context
Outlier Birnbaum's Potentialism -
a metaphysics theory
Q4P$\infty \rightarrow$ C+ $\rightarrow$ E+

POTENTIALISM THEORY

wraps-around
- and complements -
iconic Einstein's Relativity -
macro-physics theory
$E = mc^2$

Something from Nothing?

Creation ex nihilo?

Not exactly.

More precisely,
Creation ex Potential
(Creation out of Potential)

But is Potential *something* or *nothing*?

Depends on how you look at it.

As noted,
Potential is Eternal - **By definition.**
Indeed, it is ***self-evident*** that Potential is Eternal.

And, Potential/Possibility is ***the only 'something'***
which occupies this unique (eternal) conceptual space.

Thus, we have our suspect.

see 2-part https://www.youtube.com/watch?v=rKPv8zApee0 for tangential

our 'Smart Universe' driven by our hypothesized *natural force* (Q4P)

Alignments

the informal political line-ups

THE OLD GUARD:
Randomnists / neo-Darwinists* / New Atheists** / Old Eugenicists*** / British Chauvinists

v.

THE NEW GUARD:
ADVOCATES FOR: Intelligent Design / Directional Universe / Potentialism

* debunked by the end of 2019; the centerpiece of the theory -
    Natural Selection / Random Mutation -
    is now in its death-throes

** *rumor has it* that a cohort of the British contingent *aids, abets and enables* toxic
    gambits ongoing -
    typically via (intimidated) Research Associates - recruited semi-involuntarily
    to undermine and career-sabotage ascendant figures in "The New Guard"

*** see subtitle of Origins of Species (1859):
    "PRESERVATION OF FAVOURED RACES IN THE STRUGGLE FOR LIFE"

$Q4P^{z}$ = the Cosmic Instinct

Other Universes Postulate Matrix

Postulate #1. Universes do not simply *pop-up*

Postulate #2. There may or may not be more universes

Postulate #3. If there are other universes. they will each need-be
    (a) Potential-based - because Potential is the only eternal *something* and then
    (b) Q4P-ignited, and Q4P-driven

Postulate #4: All universes are hence ***directional.***

Why? Because, as elucidated above, there would appear to be only one eternal dynamic - Potential/Possibility - and without it *in the mix*, no universes are *making an appearance*. And *with* Potential in the mix, every single one of these universes will be quite directional and quite interesting.

As regards the Randomness play re: multiverse....

As we are aware, the Randomness crew found itself in seeming *checkmate* as a consequence of the 1999 Martin Rees book *Just Six Numbers* which demonstrated clearly *fine-tuned universe, and de facto showed **directional universe**. The direction of fine-tuned universe? seeking life.

In desperation, the Randomness crew formulated the following **attempted escape hatch**: Our universe may be directional, but our universe is a random fluke; there are infinite universes, and ours happened to hit it lucky. Meaning, (post-1999) per segments of the Randomness crew, there are Infinite -1 totally aimless universes, and 1 fine-tuned universe (ours).

This escape hatch is fatally flawed, however.

1) As elucidated above, if there are other universes, they are ***directional***.

2) the Cosmic Order has better things to do than to waste virtually limitless energy launching infinite -1 aimlessrt (and dead-end) universes. [See also Occam's Razor, wiki]

3) Randomness does not and cannot generate a universe - even a very primitive one.

4) Classic and well-established Probability Theory would reject the "infinite -1 aimless universe theory" with the Cosmic Order ***randomly*** birthing, sustaining, and driving our extraordinary and ever-iterating universe over a 14 billion year span as a ***viable denouement***. Probability Theory can be deployed for *possibility*, not for *de facto* impossibility*.

*See Lloyd, *Programming the Universe*, Knopf, 2007, NY, p. 57:

"In fact, the chance of an ordered universe like ours arising out of random flips of a coin is so small as to be effectively zero."

'The Second Law of Thermodynamics'

can be deployed as a strong *proof positive* for

Potentialism Theory

see SecondLaw1000

For starters, after 14 billion years,
our universe is *accelerating* and *expanding*;

but, per the 'law' it should be imploding from *entropy*?

So, enter our (hypothesized) Quest for Potential™ to trump *entropy*.

The 'Law' that is not a 'Law'

The Second Law of Thermodynamics is actually not a classic 'law of physics' but, rather, a hypothesis ostensibly based on empirical findings.

But, does our *ever-expanding universe* itself not frontally contradict this lovely 'Second Law' hypothesis?

Or, are we forced to play *games* re: *closed (or isolated) systems?*

In any event, Summa Theory rescues the thermodynamics hypothesis - as Summa Theory explains the very glaring contradiction (of our ever-expanding universe).

But, the weak - and open-ended - thermodynamics hypothesis (see above) most certainly cannot undermine Summa Theory.

The 'bottom line' question might be:

Why continue to award a frail hypothesis the designation of a physics 'LAW' (of the universe), when the universe *as-a-whole (in-our-face)* belies and contradicts the core thrust of the *(currently defined and frail at-best)* hypothesis?

Is it because the Royal Society (British) - which Lord Kelvin (one of the authors of 'Second Law') presided over - may not want to undermine yet another British icon, aside from Darwin?

Chronology
of the
Universe

[hypothesis]

Core Cluster

A core custer of questions in metaphysics

........revolves around 'Eternal Origins'

Where did the 'first something' come from

How was there any 'something' other than 'nothing'?

How did we get from that 'something' to the *present day* ?

How did that 'something' lead to the 'traction' of the universe?

Is there a Prime Mover? If this Prime Mover always existed, where did this
   Prime Mover come from? [the theogony' question]

In any event, what 'something' could be 'eternal'? [the ''Eternal Origins'
   question]

And why could our profound and extraordinary universe not have 'come
   into being'
      - or been 'brought into being' - without Evil? [also part of the 'theodicy'
   question]

Is there a 'designer' of the universe? Is this 'designer' sacred or secular?

And, if there is a 'designer',
            - where did it (the 'designer') come from?
            - what is its essence
            - roughly what are the parameters of its power?
            - have we - or have we not - encountered it?

Are we actually integral to the 'designer'?

> continued

MORPHED COSMIC ORDER

What 'ignited' the (apparently pretty smart and pretty powerful) Big Bang?

Where are we 'heading'? Is there direction to the universe?

Is there/What is -
  the 'purpose' of all? [the 'teleology' question]
    - Is there an 'arrow' to the universe?
    - a 'direction'?
    - a 'meaning'?
    - a goal?

Where *do humans stand* in all of this?

What is life? Where did life come from? Is it reborn in every being - or is it one continuum flowing from Eternal Origins?

Is there a 'cosmic consciousness'? What is consciousness?

Dose Macro Physics (Einstein's gravitational physics) ever get *stitched together* with Micro Physics (Max Planck's Quantum Mechanics)?

Does 'everything' start with the Big Bang? If not, what preceded the Big Bang?

How does Dark Energy tie in with all-of-the-above?

Can there ever be any universe without Summa's Q4P$^\infty$ *in the mix*?

Does the future ever impact the present?

Does Summa's proposed Q4P∞ thesis essentially resolve all of the above simultaneously? *YES*

Does (allegedly) competing Randomness Theory resolve any of above? *NO*

Advanced Summa

Suis Generis Code?

Is Q4P$^\infty$ actually a self-generating, self-building-out, universe-spanning, quasi-alive, self-sustaining, all-embracing, all-pervading, pinnacle natural force, quasi- computer-code -

ongoing executing/building-out
the Birnbaum's *Super-Formula*

$$Q4P^\infty \rightarrow C+ \rightarrow E+$$

- from the Get-Go ?

[note: David B was a Computer Science major at CCNY Engineering.]

3 EPOCHS:

THE 3 EPOCHS TO-DATE OF OUR UNIVERSE

[3 EPOCHS, 2 BIRTHS]

I	Pure Potential
II	Infinite Quest for Potential$^\infty$
III	Potential / Reality HYBRID

'everywhere in nature'

"Algorithms and computation take place not just in computers or between computer systems but actually everywhere in nature, in atoms, in matter,..... bacteria in a cell, and neurons in the brain."

- Avi Wigderson (Israeli mathematician)
  ABEL Prize Co-Winner 3/2021
  Princeton Institute for Advanced Study
  upon learning of hs winning the ABEL Award

[reprinted from earlier in the book]

(radically-simpfied)
Trajectory
of Cosmic Order

Eternal Potential

V

$Q4P^\infty$

V

increasingly dynamic Platforms

V

Physical Universe

V

Life

V

21st Century Human Life

V

E+

CHRONOLOGY 1000

3 EPOCHS:

[3 EPOCHS, 2 BIRTHS]

I   Pure Potential

II   Infinite Quest for Potential¨

III Potential / Reality HYBRID

\# The 3 panels to-follow are intended to provide 'visual context';
\# 'Detail /explanation will be filled-in to a very limited extent
   somewhat in Chronology-of-the-Universe to-follow later
\# This entire [*epochs of the universe*] 'zone' is 'medium-risk hypothesis'

Open-ended:
manifestation: Eternal Potential Reigns Supreme

Epoch 1

PURE POTENTIAL

[a 'something'
close to nothing]

[the Cosmic Womb of Potential]

I

primordial Metaphysical

Then, concluding the epoch >

Birth #1	Epoch 1 > 2
causality:	backward causation
trigger:	leveraged buyout (of ALL future potentials) plus E+ (Extraordinariation)
mechanism	one pulse [instigated by the trigger^] (the 'Original Pulse')
birth:	birth of Q4P$^\infty$
human parallel #1:	female womb
human parallel #2:	childbirth
human parallel #3:	pulse of a human
human parallel #4:	potential of a youngster
human parallel #5:	*leveraged buyout* is a parallel mechanism in Wall Street finance; its boom in the USA was 1982-1990

concludes with the BIRTH OF Q4P

commences with the **BIRTH OF Q4P**

Epoch 2

Infinite Quest for Potential$^{\infty}$

[Q4P (is) rolling]

[Pure Metaphysical Advance]

II

Metaphysical

*

Quantum Mechanics is *front & center*

Then, concluding the epoch >

Birth #2	Epoch 2 > 3
causality:	"the VOID couldn't take it anymore"
trigger:	splitting of [METAPHYSICAL] ZERO
mechanism:	Big Bang
birth:	birth of our physical universe*
human parallel:	orgasm
20th Century parallel:	splitting of the ATOM | 'Manhattan Project' | atom bomb | exploded on/ over Hiroshima 8/6/45, then Nagasaki

see Einstein1000.com

concludes with the **BIG BANG**

* meaning, our hybrid physical-metaphysical universe

commences with the **BIG BANG**

Epoch 3

Potential / Reality
HYBRID

[Metaphysical/Physical Advance]

[Mophed Cosmic order]

III

Metaphysical / Physical

*

our current universe [work-in-progress]

denouement unclear

Chronology1000.com

The 'baby' - Quest for Potential∞ - is *'pulled'* from the cosmic womb of Potential

CHRONOLOGY 1000

The Footprint of Potential

a rough sketch

Chronology of the Universe

Eternal Origins → Present

(a metaphysics hypothesis)

introductory note: Hitherto Inscrutable Quantum Mechanics (QM) has at least two 'faces' which we are now (OCT 2017) aware of:
(a) the Potential/Possibility/Probabilistic 'face', and
(b) the Wheeler *It-from-Bit* 'face' as a prelude to the Lloyd *Bits Compute the Universe* 'face' build-out thereof

rough sketch chronology - 1.00

Eternal Potential - as opposed-to *Nothing* - defines Eternal Origins.

At Eternal Origins, *'Potential reigns supreme'.*

CWP = Cosmic Womb of Potential
(a Potentialism Theory term)

rough sketch chronology - 1.25

We are now at the *Cosmic Womb of Potential* point here

Potential is PUSHING-forth

Simultaneously,
Infinite Potential way down-the-road is PULLING - tugging at -
Eternal Potential way back at Cosmic Origins

MORPHED COSMIC ORDER

PUSH- PULL

PUSH- PULL

PUSH- PULL

the drama increases in intensity.....

the void pulsates

---

rough sketch chronology - 1.50

* Voids abhor voids
  (proposed axiom by Summas Theory)

* The void "*couldn't take it*" any more

* **Realms of Potential**
  seek/ache-for
  some realization,
  however abstract

---

rough sketch chronology - 1.75

The conjecture:

Within the primordial realms of **Potential/Possibility**
perhaps just a
single pulse of energy

which germinated from the potential future
by (hypothesized/theorized)
'backward causation' (*aka* "retrocausality")***

tracked-back and unhinged
the equilibrium of neo-nothingness....at Eternal Origins

aka a 'leveraged buyout' [a Wall Street term from the '80s]

*** i.e. a Quantum Mechanics sub-theory that future possibilities (or energy) may
somehow impact present possibilities (or energy)

see also quantum fluctuation.....vacuum state fluctuation
origin of the universe discussion/theories.

Remember, I just need just **one pulse**

rough sketch chronology - 2.00

re: *single pulse of energy*

My educated conjecture is that this (hypothesized original) single pulse is the origin of life in our universe

- and that all life to follow through the eons emanates directly from this seminal point

Meaning, coiled / infinitely nested / quest for potential /
is the *essence of Life* - then and now

Life is inextricably connected to the birth of Epoch 2
and the cluster of dynamics noted above associated with SAME
(including backward causation and leveraged buyout -
and Quantum Mechanics good-to-go)

At the inflection point between Epoch 1 and 2, the key core dynamics aligned -

"We have a pulse"

rough sketch chronology - 2.15

The cosmic drama often mirrors the individual human drama

What is true for the Cosmic Order, will often be true for the individual human

This (hypothsized) extraordinary parallel enables the metaphysician to 'peer behind' the Big Bang - *all the way back* to Eternal Origins (the Cosmic Womb of Potential)

Thus, *the plot thickens...*

rough sketch chronology - 2.25

PUSH
(at cosmic origins)

Embryonic Quest for Potential (Q4P∞)
at Cosmic Origins
pushes-forth *...inexorably demanding* its **potential** be realized

PULL
(from the future)

Embryonic celestial potential *eons down the road aches-for and seeks fulfillment,
and incessantly* **beckons** Q4P,...**entreats** Q4P
to emerge - at long last - from the
cosmic womb of Potential... at Eternal Origins

MORPHED COSMIC ORDER

CWP = Cosmic Womb of Potential
(a Potentialism Theory term)

rough sketch chronology - 2.50

primordial dynamics

.... *the drama continues*

- along a *fault-line* of the cosmic womb of Potential

The Cosmic Womb of Potential
at this point is at max stress

Wave upon wave of Eternal Potential *vectors towards the intense drama*

Push-Pull

Push-Pull

The present - at Eternal Origins - 'pushes forward' to actualize Potential

The future - tracking towards infinity - 'beckons-forth' aching and yearning to view
actualized Potential *peeking over the horizon*

Will this interminable *cosmic tension* ever see resolution?

Push-Pull

Push-Pull

ad infinitum?

eons upon eons pass by......

critical mass is achieved

the 'tipping point'.....

The Pulse

The 'baby' - Quest for Potential™ - *'is pulled'* from the cosmic womb of Potential

the heavens witness in awe

The long-yearned-for 'birth' of the inexorable metaphysical DRIVER

Bereshith

rough sketch chronology - 2.75

Quantum Mechanics is, of course, *a vast blueprint*

But, this (theoretical) blueprint has a sub-blueprint (or a major dimension)
for equations of **Potential** dove-tailing off of 'actual' Eternal Potential

Simultaneous with the Push-Pull drama,
primordial Quantum Mechanics *pegs-off-of* the **Eternal Potential**
of primordial universe - and *vice versa*

The two **somehow** *cycle off of each other*

Meaning, Quantum Mechanics has some *modicum of life* breathed into it

The two dramas *play-out* in-concert

The net result is *'the birth of Q4P$^\infty$'*

QM = Quantum Mechanics

rough sketch chronology - 3.00

The interplay of **Eternal Potential** and Primordial Quantum Mechanics (QM)
→ yields Infinite Quest for Potential (Q4P$^\infty$)

The chronology/trajectory/direction/purpose/teleology/arc
of the universe
will follow the axis of my hypothesized/proposed*** SuperFormula

Q4P$^\infty$ → C+ → E+

Quest for Potential$^\infty$ → Complexification → Extraordinariation

see SuperFormula1000.com

*** proposed 2005 in Summa II / section: Direction of the Universe

---

QM = Quantum Mechanics

rough sketch chronology - 4.00

The interplay of **Q4P$^\infty$** and Primordial QM → yields the Wheeler *It-from-Bit* face of
QM.......
Then the build-out of the Wheeler face,
     the Lloyd *computing* face of QM,

evolves

THUS, further *filling-out* pre-Big Bang QM

QM = Quantum Mechanics

rough sketch chronology - 5.00

Q4P / pre-Big Bang Q4P∞ plots its escape
from the metaphysical void →
metaphysical cum reality (our evolving universe)

our 'Smart Universe' driven by our hypothesized *natural force* (Q4P)

rough sketch chronology - 6.00

Q4P / Igniting Big Bang Q4P∞ splits the (hypothesized) *Zero-Point* and ignites the Big
Bang.

[The Big Bang 13.8 billion years ago.]

Meaning, **Potential**,
not *Random Chance*,
and not some spontaneous genesis - *per* Wheeler and his disciple Lloyd -
ignites the entire dynamic at Eternal Origins

[From a metaphysical perspective, splitting the *Zero-Point*, as well yields polarities:
Matter:Anti-Matter... Pluses:Minuses... Good:Evil... *proto-Female:proto-Male... et al.....*]

rough sketch chronology - 6.50

It was necessary (for **Q4P∞**) to instigate/trigger/create
our universe
inasmuch as Q4P∞ needed
an extraordinary PLATFORM
- with a very substantial material/physical dimension -
to more fully play-out
Q4P∞ → C+ → E+

Meaning,
metaphysical realms alone were not a dynamic-enough PLATFORM
to optimize the advancements sought -
including the rate, diversity, complexity, richness, and quality
of advance sought

rough sketch chronology - 7.00

Q4P∞/QM is the prime catalyst on stage choreographing the unfolding universe production; it has vast influence....

rough sketch chronology - 8.00

Q4P∞ trumps Entropy
and sustains the advance of our universe.

rough sketch chronology - 8.50

[Evolution in a snapshot]

Lloyd elucidates the Quantum - # information (bit) build-out
                                # computing
                                # programming

aspect/dimension of Quantum Mechanics

Let us now throw in a fourth component -

                (Quantum) # engineering   (my concept/term)
into the mix*

One can assign the term Quantum Engineering to the entire 4-component *basket* (noted just-above).

Quantum Potential Engineering   per Potentialism Theory

# information (bit) build-out	per Lloyd
# computing	per Lloyd
# programming	per Lloyd
# engineering	per Birnbaum

The full Quantum Engineering *basket* is fused into Q4P∞, at latest by the Big Bang ignition point

Now we have 'replaced' Darwinism

Post- Big Bang (14.8 billion years ago)
Q4P∞ then drives the evolution of the universe,
and then - post the formation of our planet 4.5 billion years ago -
the evolution of Evolution.

MORPHED COSMIC ORDER

(see Evolution1000.com for fuller presentation)

* I presume that Lloyd did not want to tangle with the neo-Darwinists

rough sketch chronology - 9.00

Q4P∞ choreographs the grand cosmic drama/trajectory which includes, among other components,
exploding stars across the heavens → elements → life forms on earth → 21st Century humans and their ever-advancing consciousness

rough sketch chronology - 10.00

Q4P∞ (or a derivative thereof) is the Cosmological Constant identified by Albert Einstein in 1917*; Einstein theorized the Cosmological Constant as the counter-force to gravity's otherwise inevitably imploding the universe. [Actually, it is reverse, i. e. Gravity slows down the forward march of the Cosmological Constant *aka* Lambda.]

rough sketch chronology - 11.00

The Cosmological Constant [**Q4P∞**] has become identified with the *simplest form* of Dark Energy (Wiki / Cosmological Constant / Oct 22, 2017]

[note: The Cosmological Constant is also known by a shorthand notation lambda, or Λ]

rough sketch chronology - 12.00

"In physical cosmology and astronomy, dark energy [**Q4P∞**] is an unknown form of energy which is hypothesized to permeate all of space, tending to accelerate the expansion of the universe." [Wiki / Dark Energy / Oct 22, 2017]

[So,
the Cosmological Constant = lambda = Λ = (simple) dark energy = a salient & manifest derivative of **Q4P∞**]

see also inter-related scientific discussions - *the Fifth Force.... Quintessence*

YES / By ~2019 - thirty-one years after Summa I - elements of the scientific community are inching closer to Q4P∞

rough sketch chronology - 13.00

"Assuming that the standard model of cosmology is correct, the best current measurements indicate that dark energy [**Q4P**$^\infty$] contributes 68.3% of the total energy in the present-day observable universe." [Wiki / Dark Energy / Oct 22, 2017]

rough sketch chronology - 14.00

"Dark energy [**Q4P**$^\infty$] is the most accepted hypothesis to explain the observations since the 1990s indicating that the universe is expanding at an *accelerating rate*." [Wiki Dark Energy / Oct 22, 2017]

Meaning,
no Dark Energy [**Q4P**$^\infty$], then the Big Crunch [imploding universe]
sufficient Dark Energy [**Q4P**$^\infty$], then Expanding universe

Meaning, as well, that Potential [**Q4P**$^\infty$] is the *prime determinant* of the ultimate denouement of the universe; not gravity; not entropy; and most certainly not randomness

rough sketch chronology - 15.00

At every stage/step of the unfolding Cosmic drama/order
- from Eternal Origins thru the present day (and onward) -
Q4P$^\infty$ - the hitherto undiscerned dynamic -
is front & center, and, indeed, *the driving dynamic.*

Q4P$^\infty$ is the metaphysical *spinal column* of the *arc of the universe.*

See Inductive1000.com / 40+ page inductive proof

See Deductive1000.com / initial and partial deductive buttress

* In 1929 (Berlin) Einstein incorrectly retracted his 1917 hypothesis; but the scientific community has upheld the original (1917) hypothesis.

personal note: Both of our families lived in Berlin in 1929, and both emigrated to the USA in the 1930s, Einstein in March 1933 (while lecturing in CA → Princeton, NJ), and Birnbaum in October 1938 (pre-Kristallnact, Berlin → Madison, WISC)

Q4P$^\infty$ = the Cosmic Instinct

BTW

Your *Life Force* flows unimpeded - in a slightly circuitous line - directly from Epoch 1.

Q4P$^\infty$

So, is Q4P$^\infty$

    a, b, c or d ?

a) Quest for - P$^\infty$

b) [Quest for Potential] $^\infty$

c) [Quest for (Quest for - P$^\infty$)] $^\infty$

d) a different permutation

Summa Metaphysica I was published in 1988.

My considered judgment is that Q4P$^\infty$ is option (c).

    [Quest for (Quest for - P$^\infty$)] $^\infty$

Thus, its extraordinary power.

POTENTIALISM THEORY 1988

Q4P$^\infty$

Q4P$^\infty$ → C+ → E+

Gaia Hypothesis

The authentic synergistic dynamics — which Gaia's hypothesizers have been *pivoting off* of —
are actually the local (Planet Earth quadrant) manifestations of universe-spanning Q4P∞ playing-out the [Potentialism] SuperFormula (see SuperFormula1000.com) on Earth.

*

"The mob" - the reactionary alliance of
SELF SELECTING -
British jingoists - Darwinists - Randomnists - Hard Line Atheists -
has *fought to the death* Gaia's (correct) core proposition. As per their usual nefarious tactics, the pro-Darwinists endeavor to swarm, defame and de-legitimize directional universe theorists. Not via the force of argument, but rather by planting snarky articles, academic blackmail and reputational rape. All under the enabling blessing of the British government - and the Royal Society (London). At all costs - and by any means - upholding the (*dead man walking*) theory of Britain's favorite son Darwin.

By its usual 'sleight of hand', "the mob" endeavors to debase Lovelock (the Gaia formulator) and explain all via (fatally-flawed) Natural Selection/ Random Mutation - whose advocates - including the Cambridge University (alma mater of Darwin) ecosystem - have bullied the Western academic world - and stunted the advance of science - for well-over 100 years.

The Second Law of Thermodynamics

is a buttress for Potentialism Theory (Q4P∞)

**If no Q4P∞
the universe should have imploded
a long, long time ago
from entropy**

*

Pre - Summa / Potentialism Theory
Second Law seemingly had a problem
with our universe expanding for billions of years.

**Why did Second Law's *entropy*
not constrict and/or implode this expanding entity?**

Enter Potentialism's Q4P∞

Major Problems in [establishment] Science
- [all now clearly resolved by Summa Theory]

Selected Quotes from
ON BEING[*a]
by Dr. Peter Atkins[*b]

Celebrated atheist Oxford U scientist Peter Atkins
[2011] admits that [establishment] science remains
stymied by a series of important questions (see just-
below);
however, Potentialism [1988, 2005, 2014, 2020]
elegantly hypothesizes [integrated] answers to all of them.
See, in particular, www.Chronology1000.com
printed in Summa IV [2020].

As well, the [widely-circulated]
Huffington Post piece (June 10, 2015)
"David Birnbaum Cracks the Cosmic Code"
(see www.HuffPost1000.com)
addresses the core issues of Atkins' angst.

"The first great question of being is one that has probably
entertained us all at one time or another: where did it, the
universe, all come from? How did it begin?..." (p. 1)

"There are, in fact, three related profound questions to
address in the context of creation. One is the mechanism

of the coming into being of the universe: what actually happened at the beginning? Another is whether there is any meaning to the question of what preceded the universe and had, in some sense, the potential to become a universe. Here we are confronted by the linguistically and conceptually engaging question of whether absolutely nothing can have potency to become something. The third is whether an agent was needed to trigger the process of cosmogenesis, the process of turning that nothing into what is to all appearances something, or can nothing turn itself into something on its own? All three questions sound as though they might fall within the range of science to answer. A fourth question, why there is a universe, is rather different, but still apparently very interesting...." (p. 2)

"As a result of their intrinsic caution, almost every scientist is wisely unwilling to express a view about the events accompanying the inception of the universe. Quite honestly, they haven't a clue...." (p. 5)

"The task before science in this connection will be to show how something can come from nothing without intervention. No one has the slightest idea whether that can happen and, if so, how it can come about...." (p. 11)

"The unfolding of absolutely nothing—what out of reverence for the absence of anything, including empty space, we are calling Nothing—into something is a problem of the profoundest difficulty and currently far beyond the reach of science. It is, however, a target at which science must aim even though to some, even to scientists of a pessimistic or perhaps just realistic bent, it would seem to be for ever out of science's reach...." (p. 12)

"Presumably before the creation, when there was Nothing, there was no charge; so the coming into being of the universe was accompanied by the separation of 'no charge' into opposites. Charge was not created at the creation: electrical Nothing separated into equal and opposite charges...." (pp. 13-14)

"I promised to return to the question of *why* there is a universe. What is its purpose? Something so big, complex, and all embracing some hold, must be there for a reason...." (p. 18)

"...science is a ceaseless probing with a view to overturning authority....science, though delighted by the glorious complexity of the world, seeks the simplicity that lies beneath it....science is extraordinarily difficult, as it seeks covert mechanism....science is ever thrusting forward, wriggling into new modes of understanding,...science gives an opportunity for humanity to achieve the aspirations it already has and opens its eyes to new ones...." (pp. 26-27)

"A scientist, the arch-descendent of Occam, looks first for the simplest explanation, then builds elaborations only if the explanation's barren, rocky simplicity proves inadequate...." (p. 33)

"One problem with evolution is how it began. Competition between primitive organisms is all very well, the triumph of one message over another,
but how did matter step across the national bridge from the inorganic to the organic in the first place?
...It would be much more satisfying—satisfying of curiosity, intellectually satisfying, and possibly spiritually satisfying—if we could find a physical process by which

that gap was bridged, presumably without the apparent intervention of an agent...." (pp. 38-39)

"...Scientists are still puzzled about how this complexity [of life] emerged under the impact, presumably, of natural selection, and it remains a problem of evolution. That is not to say that there are not many ideas about how it came about. Just as for the origin of life itself, which is still a real puzzle, evolutionary biologists are not without ideas, but have not yet identified which, if any, is valid...." (pp. 60-61)

[a] Peter Atkins, *On Being*
(Oxford, England: Oxford University Press, 2011),
pp.1-2, 5, 11-14, 18, 26-27, 33, 38-39, 60-61.

[b] Scientist Peter Atkins is the author of almost 70 books, including *Galileo's Finger: The Ten Great Ideas of Science, Four Laws That Drive the Universe,* and the world-renowned textbook *Physical Chemistry*. A Fellow of Lincoln College, University of Oxford, he has been a visiting professor in France, Israel, New Zealand, and China, and continues to lecture widely throughout the world.

He is, as well, a 'poster boy' for Atheism.

the Q4P-universe-spanning-WEB-of-code
expands/advances in-tandem >

POTENTIALISM THEORY

with the universe expansion -
which it has instigated

Summa humbly offers

a bullet-proof metaphysics
[see Inductive1000.com for a 40-page inductive proof
published in/on Academia.edu]

a totally original & authentic metaphysics
[see Testimonials1000.com]

a metaphysics packaged with its own Super-Formula
[Q4P° > C+ > E+]
spanning Macro and MIcro levels
of the Cosmic Order
from time immemorial

a metaphysics with the same dynamic -
its 'spinal column',
Potential -
arching from
Eternal Origins to the Present -

a metaphysics which brazenly
peeks-behind the Big Bang
[see Chronology1000.com]
- and discovers two additional epochs

A metaphysics which frontally addresses -
and hopefully, elegantly resolves -
the top questions in cosmology/metaphysics
in a unified and elegant manner
[see HuffPost1000.com]
[see panel in Chronology1000 - 'Major Problems']

a metaphysics with no *bona fide* competing theory
[see Chronological1000.com]
[Where is the competing Metaphysics?]

a metaphysics which has *stood the test of time*
[since Summa 1 was published in 1988]
[see panel in Chronology1000
- "No flaw has been discerned']

a quite-heavily-testimonialed metaphysics
[see SummaCoverage.com]

Each still 'directional'

There *may or may not be other universes;*
but, per Summa Theory,
any palatable universe must individually *still be 'directional'* -
and Q4P$^\infty$-drven

As we have seen.,
over the past 5+ millennia,
only a Q4P$^\infty$-driven-universe
can, indeed, be *'critically understood'*

NO Q4P$^\infty$; no universe
YES, Q4P$^\infty$; maybe a full-fledged universe
        work-in-progress

Respectfully, nihilists and *fellow travelers*
trying to explain-away our own universe
as a consequence of (random) chance -
and the *roll-of-the-dice* of hypothesized random multiverse -
fail the test of *critical analysis.*

The Super-Formula*

\# was featured on the back cover of Scientific American
on our ad - September 2017 issue;
so over four years ago - *with no challenge whatsoever to-date*
[see TheoryAd1000.com for latest ad iteration]

\# the Super-Formula would seem to provide an interesting
unifying guideline for the cosmic unfolding
from Eternal Origins > the Big Bang > the Present > the Future
[see Super-Formula1000.com]

\# Even in isolation, the Super-Formula offers a Unified Theory of the Cosmos
[see TTOE1000.com]
- which works

\# wraps-around $E = mc^2$
[see Einstein1000.com]

\# Perhaps it offers 'some advantages' over
(1000 percent vacuous)
Theory of No Theory - *Randomness*

* $Q4P^\infty \rightarrow C+ \rightarrow E+$

Super-Formula1000.com

THE METAPHYSICIST AS
DETECTIVE

(cracking the cosmic code)

\#   connecting the dots / discerning patterns

example:

$$Q4P^{\infty} \rightarrow C+ \rightarrow E+$$

[see Super-Formula1000.com]

\#   buying into the conjecture that
the universe and *the human*

parallel each other

thus, one can endeavor to extrapolate 'missing pieces'
one-from-the-other

example:

the human emerges from the womb;
the universe emerges from the Cosmic Womb of Potential

The Visual Horizon

There is a limit - 'the visual horizon' - of how far back in time 'science' can 'see', i.e. there is a limit to 'visualization'..

Essentially, of course, the 'limit' is the Big Bang (13.8 billion years ago) - and the *cosmic microwave background (CMB) radiation*(discovered 1964 is the '*trace evidence*'.

Now, physicists, like all of us, like visual evidence, testability, and supporting equations - so scientists are on very uncomfortable ground in peering behind the Big Bang.

Indeed, scientists, in particular, are not wired for doing so

But this is not shocking; it is rare for an individual or a cohort (like scientists) to be adroit both in the physical sciences - and, simultaneously in conceptual/creative fields (like metaphysics incorporating the pre-Big Bang time zone.)

Possible (to be really good at both), but improbable.

MIT students do not necessarily do great at Harvard - and *vice versa*

First Key:
Now, the first key to the solution of *peering behind the veil* of the Big Bang - is to *discern / isolate*-on an eternal dynamic - if there is one.

This I have allegedly done, as you are aware. (Potential, per my series Summa Metaphysica, is eternal.)

Once one has isolated on that dynamic (Potential), one can, *so to speak reverse-engineer* the Cosmic Order. <<< my educated conjecture

But *how/where* does one start?

Second Key:
Well, the next *key to the kingdom* is the following:

Humans mimic the Cosmic Order - and vice versa; the two are *mirror images*.*
<<< my educated conjecture

Thus, one can potentially often fill-in gaps in our understanding of each (humans, Cosmic Order) - by examining/dissecting its *mirror image*..

This (*mirror imaging*) is an 'imprecise science', but it gives us a powerful tool.- if used in conjunction with the right Working Hypothesis.
[Yes, we assert that Potentialism Theory is the appropriate Working Hypothesis.]

* Per Jewish doctrine, albeit a doctrine not our focus here, the human is created *b'zelem Elokim - in the image of God*

The Cambrian Explosion

and our Theory

Earth: formed: ~4.5 billion years ago

Cambrian explosion: ~ 0.5 billion years ago

'....an event approximately 541 million years ago in the Cambrian period
when most major animal phyla appeared in the fossil record.
It lasted for about 13 – 25 million years
and resulted in the divergence of most modern metazoan phyla.
The event was accompanied by major diversification of other organisms.' ***

So, focusing on Q4P∞, what is happening in this picture?

My best assessment is that for Q4P∞. the first 4 billion (post-formation of Earth)
year period was 'schooling' / 'warm-up'

Q4P∞ experimented and learned; it steadily advanced *up the slope* of the
learning curve

At the Cambrian point, Q4P∞ *made-its-move*

It had just tested the gears for Complexification for 4 billion years -
and Q4P∞ astutely integrated the new-found knowledge

At Cambrian it *mustered its powers* - and choreographed/designed a new
platform for Extraordinariation - the explosion of diversified organisms...

*** Cambrian Explosion / WIKI / 1/22/20

THE INTER-RELATIONSHIP

What are some components of the interrelationship between
the universe ~Life Form
to (the somehow tethered/integrated) humans?

On different levels, each, of course, respectively seeks C+, and onto E+

The universe

seeks-after...aches-for...maneuvers-for -
the widest/richest/most intense possible C+ and then E+

*

The universe is many billions of years old,
and a typical human (currently) has a life span of under 100 years
but
the typical human (and its cohort) is the vehicle through which the
universe vicariously has (ever-richer) **emotion** and related (ever-
expansive) **consciousness**, as we know it **

** [And, *in the mix*, does the universe vicariously, as well, explore religiosity and/or
spirituality? Perhaps.]

*

21st CENTURY PUBLISHING
150+ AUTHORS/SCHOLARS

continue >

MORPHED COSMIC ORDER

Section I

MORPHED COSMIC ORDER

*"I am inclined to think that Summa Metaphysica
is the dawn of a period of metaphysical revision"*

POTENTIALISM THEORY

- Prof. Lawrence Schiffman, NYU
[pinnacle *'Influencer'*,
Jewish thought, philosophy, history, talmudic literature]

Q4P$^\infty$ is the major building-block
of CHI = Life Force

POTENTIALISM THEORY

Q4P$^\infty$ and CHI are inextricably bound

---

the Birnbaum Teleology

Q4P∞ > C+ > E+

POTENTIALISM THEORY

the - formula / direction / purpose / path / arrow
of our universe

The Birnbaum super-formula
offers an overarching Cosmology -
and macro/micro Metaphysics -
of the universe

POTENTIALISM THEORY

wrapping-around
Einstein's macro-physics formula
of the universe

(Respectfully) Birnbaumian Evolution Theory

POTENTIALISM THEORY

is free of the (ultimately *fatal*) flaws
in [iconic, but doomed]
Darwinian Evolution Theory
(and its Modern Synthesis heirs)

MORPHED COSMIC ORDER

Quantum Mechanics (QM) v. Q4P

It is far from clear where QM ends and where Q4P starts.

And it is far from clear whether there is 1% overlap or 100% overlap (at this point).

And it is far from clear if/how the overlap % has morphed over the eons.

Simply put, we do not know the precise relationship -
and if/how that relationship has morphed.

just one dynamic

**Potentialism Theory deploys
just one (hypothesized) dynamic - Q4P -
across the depth and breadth of cosmic history.**

**Meaning, just this one overarching dynamic-
Quest for Potential∞ -
has driven the universe,
through this day**

start:
Deductive1000.com

**The initial and partial
hard physics proof
for Potentialism Theory**

Lambda ≈ Dark Energy ≈ Cosmological Constant ≈ Q4P, per Summa Theory.

Lambda = salient Q4P$^\infty$

Λ

Lambda

the Cosmological Constant

Einstein (1917) hypothesized that there was a dynamic countering gravity's pull on the planets; else the planets would crunch together.

Einstein identified this dynamic as the Cosmological Constant.

The world scientific community would later call this force Lambda.

In reality (per Potentialism Theory) Einstein (1917) had the concept correct, but the seqence/alignment backwards.

The correct seqence/alignment is:
1. **Lambda** is driving the universe to expand outward;
2. **Gravity** is *putting the brakes* on Lambda.

Now, Lambda is salient Q4P,
or in other words
Lambda is Q4P somewhat 'showing its hand'.
(Elusive) Lambda, in turn, is manifested 'saliently' via Dark Energy.

Lambda, of course, is just the 'visible'
"tip of the iceberg" of infinite Quest for Potential$^\infty$ (Q4P$^\infty$).

Thus, while Volume I of my metaphysics series (Summa Metaphysica) proposing Quest for Potential is copyrighted 1986, Einstein discerned Lambda in 1917; he did not realize - and never realized - that he had hit 'the mother lode' (i.e. the *'driver of the Cosmic Order'*).

For the record,

In 1929,
Einstein (in error) rejected his own *Cosmological Constant* concept, calling it his 'biggest blunder'. [Actually, he was right the first time (1917).]

In the 1990s,
New studies confirm that the *Cosmological Constant* is the best fit for Dark Energy, and offers the most precise and accurate estimate yet of its value.

In 2018,
The current standard model of cosmology is known as the `Lambda-CDM model`.

However, maintream science, in parallel to Einstein (1917), still has the sequence/alignment of the dynamics backwards: See line 4 near top: "In reality...

＊

As of Fall 2018, in physical cosmology and astronomy, Dark Energy (≈ Lambda) is considered an unknown form of energy which is hypothesized to permeate all of space, and which is accelerating the expansion of the universe. [Summa / Potentialism Theory, of course, hypothesizes *same* (1988 →) for Q4P.]

Discerned, Identified, Calculated & Measured

Lambda = salient Q4P$^\infty$

Λ
Scientifically Discerned

The scientific community &
the inadvertent 100+ year *hard science* unfolding/discovery
of key components of Potentialism Theory

So, *Lambda ≈ Dark Energy ≈ Cosmological Constant ≈ Q4P, per Summa Theory.*

Lambda was discerned / identified initially by Einstein in 1917,
but has emerged (by 2018) front & center in astrophysics
via the '**Lambda-CDM Model**'
(the *standard model* of Big Bang cosmology).

Meaning, Q4P∞ is de facto embedded in - and integral-to - the current *standard model* of cosmology

So,
re: The Cosmological Constant ≈ Lambda ≈ Dark Energy ≈ Q4P, per Summa

1) It was introduced, discerned & calculated (as noted, initially by Einstein, 1917).

2) The best current measurements indicate that Dark Energy contributes 68.3 percent of the total energy of the present-day observable universe.

3) Dark Energy's density has been precisely measured (apparently ~7 x 10^{-30} g/cm^3)

4) It is clearly key in driving the universe forward.

5) The current *standard model* scientific theory has Lambda literally starting its title

So, scientifically measured on multiple fronts, placed front & center in the *standard model* title, and generally accepted as driving the universe forward.

Is not Lambda thus direct 1:1 corroboration of a key slice of Potentialism Theory?

Lambda ≈ Dark Energy ≈ Cosmological Constant
is thus the scientifically (measurable /measured) manifestation of Q4P.

Not bad having key components one's (revolutionary) metaphysics/ cosmology theory *de facto* scientifically discerned over a 101 year period (1917 to date).

So, Einstein tripped-over Q4P in 1917, but misread its overarching power and centrality.

And the scientific community at-large has yet to grasp Lambda's full dimensions.

*

The Cosmological Constant's identification (1917) by Einstein (hence, the discovery of a 'physical' manifestation of Summa's Q4P), is the rough equivalent of Sir Arthur Eddington's (May 29, 1919) solar eclipse proof of Einstein's curvature of space time theory.

Except that, as noted, in Einstein's (Cosmological Constant) case, he radically missed the full import.

*

Psychologically and scientifically, Einstein was fixated on gravity as the central motif of the Cosmic Order; thus, to Einstein, other dynamics - like Lambda - essentially play supporting or reaction roles.

However, from my Potentialism-centric - and hopefully objective - view of the Cosmic Order, whereas gravity (a physical dynamic) is very central in our universe, it is trumped in importance/impact/centrality by overarching Q4P - the overarching metaphysical dynamic of the Cosmic Order.

*

I respectfully believe that Lambda crucially moves the needle on Potentialism - from *theory to partially scientifically discerned.*
And, indeed, the Lambda-CDM Model is more precisely, the Q4P-CDM Model.

In a twist of fate, Potentialism Theory was partially/inadvertently discerned & partially validated (1917) by scientific great Einstein - before the Potentialism Metaphysics/Cosmology theory was even conceptualized/presented/ disseminated (1988 and onwards) by Outsider/Outlier Birnbaum. Rumor has it that I was not even born until 1950. And via scientific advances in understanding the Cosmological Constant ≈ Dark Energy - which is actually Q4P Energy, the academic establishment has advanced our scientific knowledge of Potentialism Theory, and to some partial extent, validated it.

*

Thus, the mainstream academic community may want the interloper (Birnbaum) to stop messing in their turf with his over-the-top theory; but they have unwittingly albeit scientifically - and from multiple angles - given significant scientific evidence and buttress - over a 100-year span - to Summa's *avant-garde* theory (1988 →).

Put another way, the establishment academic community has radically strengthened Potentialism's position on the metaphysics/cosmology chessboard. With respect, there is no known theory which can successfully challenge Potentialism.

Lambda = salient Q4P$^\infty$

The Misnomer
'Dark Energy'

The correct appellation would be:
Salient Q4P$^\infty$ Energy
or
SQE

'Dark Energy' is meaningless in this astrophysics arena;
there is nothing *dark* about it

'Salient Q4P$^\infty$ Energy' ('SQE') is meaningful - and precise.

The Boss

Lambda = salient Q4P$^\infty$

Lambda

an integral part
of the over-arching cosmic dynamic

Einstein and scientists to follow tend to view Lambda as a stand-alone
dynamic;
however, Lambda is just a salient portion of overarching Q4P$^\infty$;
and that is part of the reason that Einstein *et al.* have such great difficulty
with Lambda.

Q4P$^\infty$ reigns supreme
and Lambda is just a salient segment of it.

The Birnbaum *super-formula*

$$Q4P^∞ → C+ → E+$$

Quest for Potential$^∞$ → Complexification → Extraordinatiation

a *suis generis* infinitely nested algorithm

[the inviolate arc of the universe]

an infinitely iterative dynamic

[the full-spectrum macro & micro level
common denominator trajectory
of the Cosmic Order]

the eternal - **teleology / *chi* / direction / *modus operandi*** - of the universe

The Grand Alliance:

Q4P and QM-related

The alliance / collaboration / quasi-fusion of

Q4P
with
QM-related:

QM (Quantum Mechanics)
AI (the AI dimension of QM)
ML (the 'Machine Learning')
dimensions of our universe
and integral
genome engineering by the 'alliance'

ultimately yields >

21st century humans

and the current dynamic
work-in-progress
particular state of our universe -

iterating/complexifying,
of course,
by the moment

global education network

The superlaw of potentialism:

Posted by Garem | July 10, 2014

Q4P > E+: The overarching dynamic of the Cosmic Order

The Quest for Infinite Potential is a ground-breaking, theory of cosmology
for the 21st Century. Envisioned by private scholar and metaphysicist
David Birnbaum, its principles are laid out in the three part series, Summa
Metaphysica I, II and III (Ktav, 1988; New Paradigm Matrix, 2005; New Paradigm
Matrix, 2014). See www.SummaMetaphysica.com.

Birnbaum states that the universe is driven by an inherent need to grow ever
increasingly more Complexification – more complex/sophisticated/varied/
wondrous.
This Complexification (shorthand notation: C+) is driven by one simple 'axiom':
Quest for Potential seeks-after Extraordinariation, or symbolically by formula:
Q4P > E+.

This overarching dynamic expresses that the Quest for Infinite Potential (Q4P) in
all things in the universe follows a scripted path towards Extraordinariation (E+).
E+ itself Birnbaum describes as the ultimate state of Complexification.
Birnbaum uses his coined term of Complexification to distinguish it from mere
complexity. (Simple) complexity is an expression of the mechanistic complexity
of a system – the workings of molecular bonding, the organic complexity of
living entities, etc. Complexification covers both measurable complexity as well

as more abstract complexity – human emotion, reason, spirituality, altruism, etc. But the very nature of the Potential dynamic lends itself to be both the foundations of Cosmic Law as well as the Cosmic Drive (see Potentialismtheory. com).

Potentialism is the central drive of the cosmos. It permeates every facet of existence. It is omnipresent and it is pervasive. From the formation of life to the more abstract formation of reason and art, it's hand in creation can always be witnessed. Birnbaum states that the universe continually changes and that change is governed by the Quest for Infinite Potential. It is not only a universal, infinite drive – but it is the only drive. There is nothing in the universe that cannot be explained in terms of Potential-driven Complexification. But the very nature of Potential begs the question as to the origins of the laws themselves which govern the universe.

As discussed, Potential not only drives Complexification, but it does so with intention – towards universal Extraordinariation. That much can be seen by simply observing the direction of evolution as well as unfolding complexity on a day to bay basis. From the splitting of cells, to the birth of a child, to the growing, higher reasoning of a developing human. More interesting though, is observing Complexification unfolding within the laws of the universe itself. It begs the question – How is the nature of mathematics, physics, chemistry and biology just perfect to allow complexity to unfold as it needs to?

The answer is profound in its simplicity. The laws of physics, like every other thing in the universe, are driven by Potential as well. To put it simply, the laws are optimized because, as a rule of Potentialism, they must be. There was never an alternative because the universe itself, as a whole, must strive towards Extraordinariation. It cannot seek a "near perfect" level of Extraordinariation – that will never suffice. Only one end-goal will do – perfect Extraordinariation however elusive that horizon-goal might be.
If the atomic forces were any stronger or weaker, atoms could not have formed properly. If atoms bonded differently, the necessary molecular structures we see now could not have been created – thus humanity could not have existed. But humanity itself is a necessary stepping stone in cosmic evolution. So humanity had to happen. Potential follows Extraordinariation, there is no runner up or secondary path that will do.

To Potentialists, the laws of the universe are without exception and immutable. They are eternal and unchanging. That is the nature of Potentialism itself. When speaking of great changes in the universe, it may seem this rule can be broken – but this is not so. Think instead of cosmic law like a legal code – a constitution governing the universe itself. The laws themselves are permanent and unchanging. But like humans who draft a constitution, Potential has left the ability for amendments. The reasoning is the same for a human drafted constitution. It is foreseen that, in the future, situations may arise never envisioned when the original laws were drafted. For instance, in the time before molecules, it was not necessary to have a law beyond that which governed the formation of atoms.

As such, the universe leaves itself free to add new laws in response to ever increasing complexity. When the universe gelled below Planck values, physics split and crafted the laws of gravity and quantum mechanics. When temperatures cooled enough for particles to become atoms, atomic laws was born; when the environment was ready for the formation of molecules, thus was born the rules governing molecular bonding; and when human evolution was sufficiently advanced, thus was born the laws governing art and reason and emotion (see ParadigmChallenge.com).

It is the pervasive nature of Potential that gives it the ability to hide in plain sight. When something is so intrinsic in the universe, on so fundamental a level, it is easily overlooked. But Potential is both the drive for cosmic Complexification as well as the creator of the laws which govern the universe itself. It is the beginning and the end, the alpha and the omega, the drive of Potential and the distant realization of Extraordinariation (see www.SummaCoverage.com).

Birnbaum-Super-Formula

www.SummaMetaphysica.com

Quick Juxtaposition

theory	POTENTIALISM	RANDOMNESS
directional?	Directional	Non-directional
status	Challenger	Establishment
prime protagonist	Birnbaum	secretive clique
cosmic 'driver'	Cosmic Prime Mover	no 'Driver'
range	Universalistic	hard-line Atheistic
direction/teleology	Quest for Potential$^\infty$	Aimlessness
home base	USA	England
best origin date	1988, 2005, 2014	1859
known for	(directional) Q4P	(random) mutation

Q4P$^\infty$ = the Cosmic Instinct

"The Chart"
Fuller Juxtaposition
Potentialsm v. Randomness

[note: grey box signifies *problematic*]

	Issue	A	B	C
		Potentialism	(classic) Randomness	Randomness / Infinite Multiverse **hybrid**
1	Number of Data Points Supporting the Particular Formulation	trillions	0	0
2	Is the Formulation "Falsifiable"? aaa	YES	YES, but indeed found false bbb / formulation DISCREDITED	NO ddd [so, unscientific Formulation]
3	Is our own universe fine-tuned?	YES / Q4P	NO bbb / so Formulation DISCREDITED	YES
4	Consonant with Second Law of Thermodynamics? ccc	YES	NO ccc [so, major flaw in Formulation]	
5	Simultaneous Solution?	YES	NO [so, weaker Formulation]	
6	Provable Inductively?	YES fff	NO [so, weaker Formulation]	NO [so, weaker Formulation]
7	Number of Universes neccessary for Formulation	1	1	infinite∞ eee
8	*Stalking horse* for a Fundamentalist doctrine	NO	YES, for hard-line Atheism	
9	Internally contradictory?	NO	YES ggg	
10	Follows the principles of Formal Logic? hhh	YES	NO hhh	
11	Empirically observational?	YES	NO hhh	NO ii

	Issue	A	B	C
		Potentialism	(classic) Randomness	Randomness / Infinite Multiverse **hybrid**
12	Oblivious to contradictory evidence? [ii]	NO	YES [iii]	
13	A 'centerpiece text'?	SUMMA	?	?
14	A *core equation* presented?	YES Q4P → C+ → E+	NEVER	**NOT YET**
15	Universe origin / catalyst & calibration of Big Bang	Q4P via the quantum calibrated the move and ignited the universe [kkk]	random	NO
16	directional	YES	NO	actually partially directional [mmm]
17	diversity of phenomena the formulation can explain	ALL	NONE	
18	'connects the dots'	YES, all	NO, none	
19	explanatory capability	YES full-spectrum	NONE. *explanatory impotence*	
20	linked-to	Quantum Mechanics	nihilism, hard-line Atheism	
21	A 'higher force' exists	YES	NO; contemptuous of idea;	
22	compatible-with discovery science [ppp]	YES	NO	
23	patterns to the universe	YES	NO; contemptuous of idea	
24	direction to the universe	YES	NO; contemptuous of idea	
25	'direction to the universe' provable?	YES center section C+ demonstrable [qqq]	YES / invalidates the Randomness Formulation [qqq]	
26	Core of Theory provable?	provable / see C+ [qqq]	proven wrong from two directions: 1999: Fine-tuned Universe (Rees) 2005: C+ directional (Birnbaum)	

MORPHED COSMIC ORDER

	Issue	A	B	C
		Potentialism	(classic) Randomness	Randomness / Infinite Multiverse hybrid
27	spirituality possible	YES	NO; contemptuous of idea	
28	*infinite divine* possible?	YES possible / possible infinite divine potential	absolutely not; not even a 'direction' to the universe is possible	
29	articles?	100+ see [qqq]	vicariously plant toxic & defamatory articles on opposing theorists in the accommodating Chronicle of Higher Education (sic) [sss]	
30	underlying world-view	universalist	doctrinaire hard-line Atheist / Fundamentalist Anti-Theist / axiomatic - No direction/pattern whatsoever to universe (excption: Evolution)	
31	Evolution	YES; but see important footnote[ttt]	YES / actually worshipful; of their deity Darwin [uuu]	
32	intellectual heir to >	Aristotelian directionality; Spinozan lattice matrix	alchemy; Emperor's Clothes fable	
33	Cosmic Origins (way back pre-pre-Big Bang)	Q4P split 'pure ZERO' Into positive and negative bits [yyy]	no clue	
34	Cosmology?	Q4P → C+ → E+ [qqq]	clueless / worship Randomness	
35	Teleology	same Q4P → C+ → E+ [qqq]	clueless / worship Randomness	
36	Cosmic Goal?	E+ Extraordinariation [qqq]	clueless / worship Randomness	
37	Is formullation- bullet-proof or bullet-ridden	bullet-proof [www]	bullet-ridden [xxx]	
38	structurally textbook *'scientific'*?	YES	NO see 2, 4, 6, 8, 9, 10, 11, 12, 17, 18, 19	NO see 2, 6, 11, 17, 18, 19

Note that issues 2, 6, and 11 (just above) are inter-related;
they are each related-to '*testability*';
they are each not precisely the same.

aaa

False is bad;
Falsifiable [means, can be checked] is good.
see Falsifiability *Wiki*

bbb

see *Just Six Numbers* by Martin Rees, 1999
plus see Fine-Tuned Universe *Wiki*

ccc

The Randomness crew presents an aimless universe. But, per the Second Law of
Thermodynamics, an aimless universe with no central dynamic, should implode.
See also separate panel below - white text on blue background: The Second Law of
Thermodynamics

ddd

therefore not **scientific** / merely speculation

eee

Many observers, including this theorist, believe that even infinite∞ universes are
insufficient for their speculation. Furthermore, this hybrid firmulation will need Q4P in any
event - for the ignition, traction, sustainment and ongoing development of every single
one of these universes.

fff

see www.Inductive1000.com for 40+ page proof of Summa Theory by Mark Davis
see www.InductiveDeductive.com for article in Harvard Kennedy School Ash Center
publication

ggg

The Randomness directional and sole dynamic of Evolution contradicts its over-arching
mythology of (*non-directional*) Randomness.

hhh

Asserts a grandiose negative axiom. *In toto* the Randomness fomulation axiomatically
and cavalierly dismisses any possible direction -
physical or metaphysical - to our ordered, expanding
and accelerating universe: Have they indeed checked out every nook and cranny across
the span of our universe - across its 14 billion year span?

iii

We canot observe potential universes outside our own.

jjj

See *Just Six Numbers*, Rees (1999) *et al.*
Rees *makes the case* that the universe is fine-tuned.
See *Complexification* [C+] per Birnbaum (1988 and onwards)
[see major focus in Intro to Summa II, March, 2005;
see SuperEquation1000.com]
Potentialism Theory's posited direction of the universe is
that (Brnbaum-hypothesized) Complexification + is the core
mechanistic driver, and is, indeed, obviously directional.
See also subsequent - similar but leaner - presentation
on 'ever-increasing complexity' - per Seth Lloyd,
Programming the Universe, Knopf (2007), pps. 5, 199-200.
Of course, presumably many others have observed the basic trajectory.
So, integrating Summa and Lloyd, Complexification is a metaphysical imperative
which translates into the physical advance via quantum messaging.

kkk

Juxtaposed against Seth Lloyd, "Then all at once the universe sprang into existence".
Ibid, p. 45

mmm

Per this speculative hybrid proposition, the Cosmic Order is primed to generate infinite$^{\infty}$
universes

ppp

see Discovery Science *Wiki*

qqq

see *Superequation1000.com*

rrr

see *SummaCoverage.com*

sss

see Closing1000.com

ttt

a) The general concept of Evolution stands.
b) 'Survivability' as a necessary component stands.
c) However, Randomness *falls*
  [see Evolution1000.com]
d) Random Mutation is not the 'driver'

uuu

Even though Evolution directly contradicts Randomness (directionless)

www

No flaw whatsoever discerned; Summa I was published 1988 by KTAV,
and, notwithstanding the Randomness / Atheist 30-year agita over Potentialism Theory,
they are unable to punch a hole in it - large or small.

xxx

breaks down on multiple fronts / see this very chart / the universe is both fine-tuned and directional

yyy

Meaning, Potentialism differentiates betwen earlier Cosmic Origins and later Universe Origins.

Summa defines 'Cosmic Order' as everything-everything, metaphysical and physical; and defines
'our universe' as our known universe, Big Bang and onwards.

The clinical translation: **Randomness is quite flawed - on multiple fronts.**

The 'street' translation: **Those Randomness boys are '*peddling snake oil*'.**

MORPHED COSMIC ORDER

Section J

MORPHED COSMIC ORDER

"unparalleled and magisterial"

POTENTIALISM THEORY

Hugo van den Berg, Department Methmatics,
University of Warwick
Coventry, UK

the universe intermediate-drive

POTENTIALISM THEORY

C+ Complexification

BIRNBAUMIAN EVOLUTION

POTENTIALISM THEORY

displaces [Darwinian] Random Mutation plank
with Ultra-Sophisticated Design-Hyper-Iteration
courtesy-of Q4P$^\infty$ - a *pinnacle natural force*

the Big Bang is not the beginning of our universe;

POTENTIALISM THEORY

the Big Bang is the beginning of Epoch III of our universe
see Chronology1000.com

In its Evolutionary thrusts
Q4P$^\infty$ is not choosing the route towards *the fittest*

POTENTIALISM THEORY

Rather, it is choosing the optimal route
towards the end-goal of *the most extraordinary*

a hitherto undiscerned -

POTENTIALISM THEORY

overarching ~eternal dynamic

MORPHED COSMIC ORDER

finessing Einstein's *macro universe* with Planck's *micro universe?*

Mission Possible?

Ⓗ Universities News

ISSN 2278 - 7178

News for Universities Worldwide...

Wrapping Around Einstein

April 12, 2014

The Holy Grail of physics has always been a Unifying Theory - unifying Macro & Micro physics. (Macro-level) Relativity and (Micro-level) Quantum Mechanics leave theorists with a seemingly intractable paradox – they are both demonstrably true, yet they contradict each other. The great scientific mystery has been how two seemingly contradictory -
albeit theoretically and empirically provable theories - can be reconciled.

Metaphysical theorist and philosopher David Birnbaum may be closer than imaginable to an answer. In his three-part treatise, Summa Metaphysica I: Religious Man (1988), II: Spiritual Man (2005), and III: Secular Man (2014). [Summa IV is reportedly on the drawing board]

Birnbaum, aligned with Aristotle, presents a teleologically based (direction-based) model of the cosmic order in sharp contrast to the entrenched Theory of Randomness. His Summa Metaphysica proposes a conceptual revolution, challenging entrenched Randomness Theory. Conceptually, Birnbaum posits and defends that the universe is not driven by random-chance and decay, but rather by an intrinsic drive to advance and enhance. Without falling into a religious argument over the nature of the force of Potentialism, Birnbaum's Quest for Infinite Potential proposes and describes a driver & direction (Quest for Infinite Potential) for the cosmic order.

At its most basic, Potential is the inherent force in the universe that drives creation – matter, energy, life and evolution. It is, per Birnbaum, omnipresent and eternal. Birnbaum's Potentialism (first volume 1988) is a well-defended and vetted theory of cosmology. But the true test of the strength of a philosophical cosmological theory is whether it can stand in the face of the spectrum of physics and reality - which it has to date.

Put simply, the competing 'theory' of Randomness does not. It throws in the 'intellectual towel' before even attempting to explain physical phenomenon, (somewhat bizarrely) claiming that the entire universe is random, pointless and unknowable. By contrast, Potentialism not only accepts the myriad challenges, it welcomes them.

Einstein and Planck

Here is the fundamental issue. Einstein is the creator of the (Macro Physics) General Theory of Relativity and the (Micro Physics) Special Theory of Relativity. Relativity shows the interrelation of time and space. The Special Theory describes a geometrically flat space-time universe. This 'flat universe' is where Max Planck's Quantum Mechanics Theory lives. The basic issue with this is that the universe which Special Theory describes is *not our universe*. The Special Theory universe is a place where gravity doesn't exist. To be clear, Quantum Mechanics Theory was crafted in a universe that is not ours. Special Theory was only crafted as an intermediary step as Einstein was working on the (Macro Physics) General Theory of Relativity, which incorporates Einstein's work on space-time with the Classical Mechanical Model of physics and Newtonian Physics, which governs gravity.

The (Macro Physics) General Theory does its job. It marries space, time and gravity into one mathematical model. That Quantum Theory was born as a derivative of the Special Model was unexpected. Here lies the problem though – Quantum Theory only works in a space-time model with a flat geometry. The addition of the Newtonian physics of gravity creates bends and depressions in space-time. These depressions are not possible in Quantum Theory. At the same time, they are not possible to remove in (Macro Physics) General Relativity.

How much stranger can this get? (Micro Physics) Quantum Physics works. Not only can it describe the smallest particles of our universe, much of modern technology is based on its principles. Turning on a modern radio is proof of Quantum Mechanics. But (Macro Physics) General Relativity works as well. Time-space warping has conclusively been proven as well. Is this a mathematical mistake? Have two of the greatest minds in the history of science in reality both failed in their most important works?

Physicists say conclusively no. Hence, their exhaustive search for a Unifying Theory or what is called the (physics) Theory of Everything (ToE). What is missing for a (physics) ToE is the glue that melds these two models, or universes, together. If not a hard mathematical model, as it seems it is beyond math to explain, then a philosophical model. According to Planck and Einstein, the ToE would have to be simple and universal.

Infinite Potential

Birnbaum's Potentialism Theory Potentialism already describes such a unifying force. Birnbaum audaciously proposed (1988) that one 'simple and universal' dynamic -- the Quest for Infinite Potential -- drives creation and the laws of the universe. In the 26 years to date subsequent to Summa I no flaw has been discerned in the hypothesis. Included in Potentialism theory is the understanding that the universe of tangible reality (our universe) emerged from a grander cosmos of non-tangible reality (eternal Infinite Potential).

According to conceptual theorist Birnbaum, Quest for Infinite Potential (operating in a grander cosmic context of non-tangible reality) harnessed the eternal equations of Physics-Math to ignite our (reality) universe (via the Big Bang). In turn this symbiotic dynamic – Infinite Potential in concert with the equations – is the catalyst for biogenesis, life as we know it, evolution and consciousness: et-al The elusive (five+ millenia) 'designer' is thus discerned.

Now how does this apply to ToE (Theory of Everything)? According to Potentialism Theory, all things in the entirety of the cosmic order are simultaneously (a) what it 'is' and (b) the potential for what it 'can be.' That is, for instance, a person both (a) exists and (b) within that person exists the potential for their legacy and the ramifications of their legacy; included in their legacy are there own and achievements of all the children and *on and on* – hence the term, Infinite Potential.

Birnbaum offers a schematic: Quest for Potential (Quest for Potential (Quest for Potential.
He suggests the shorthand notation Q4P, thus the schematic would be: Q4P (Q4P (Q4P
To be able to display the formula (and the universe) succinctly: Q4P$^\infty$

How does this conceptualization apply to physics?

Let's take a classical example from Quantum Mechanics. Say we take a piece of lead and cut two slits in it and release photons towards it. Any individual photon might go through either slit. And photons are waves, so after they pass through the slits, they will collide and interfere with one another. Common sense so far. However, according to the Quantum Mechanical model, any individual photon passes through BOTH slits. This has been proven to be fact. In tests, an *individual* photon has been shown to interfere with *itself* as it simultaneously passes through both slits.

As disturbing as this phenomenon might sound, Potentialism doesn't just explain this, it predicts it. On a quantum, sub-atomic level, it is easier to witness Potentiality by inference. As *predicted*, and indeed explained by Birnbaum, the photon has the Potential to travel through either slit, hence in the quantum dimension it 'exists' passing through both until it necessarily is realized.

Potentiality and Actuality

To put things more simply, (micro-level) Quantum Mechanics describes the Potentiality of objects, (macro-level) Relativity describes their Actuality. In physics, a quanta is the minimal amount of *something* for something to happen. For instance, how much energy must be applied to make an electron move from one state of excitement to another? There is no in-between on the quantum level. It will be at excitement state #1 until enough energy is applied for it to exist at excitement state #2.

In Potentiality terms, Quantum Mechanics describes what must happen for something to exist. This is Potentiality at its most basic. Something has the Potential to exist – whether it does or doesn't. Some Quantum Mechanical phenomena simply give us an inferential glimpse at the states of Possibility. When they are observed directly and necessitated, they are actualized.

So why does Quantum Mechanics only recognize flat time-space and not curved time-space? Quantum Mechanics is in a threshold position between the quasi-metaphysical realm of Special Relativity, and the reality-realm of expressed Potentiality. General Relativity, in turn, is an actuality. It represents what the current universe is.

More than Physics

There is a veil between what 'can be' (the quasi-metaphysical) and what already 'is' (reality). Physicists are uncomfortable with this and understandably so. However, Potentialism is not only comfortable with this, it daringly predicts it (in rudimentary form back in 1988). Mathematical physics can only explain one part of the universe – what 'is' (reality). When it comes to what 'can be' – universal Potential (metaphysical and quasi-metaphysical) – it falls apart. Something more is needed.

The metaphysics of Potentialism leaves room for different universal rules for, respectively, Quantum Mechanics and Relativity. Saying that they must mathematically always agree limits Infinite Potential. It is necessary to understand that Quantum Mechanics physics is at the threshold between Potentiality and the Realization of the cosmological order; Birnbaum's Potentialism Theory is the bridge between the two.

Among other triumphs, Potentialism Theory resolves the hitherto intractable paradox noted at the very top of this piece. Thus although tucked into just one brief formula ($Q4P^\infty > C+ > E+$), for lack of a more humble term, Birnbaum's Potentialism Theory is the hitherto elusive *Theory of Everything*.

our 'Smart Universe' driven by our hypothesized *natural force* (Q4P)

RESOLVES THE PARADOX

Per Universities News (2014)*, Potentialism Theory resolves,
among other issues, the Einstein-Planck paradox.

My Chronology of the Universe exposition [Chronology1000.com],
which is published within Summa Metaphysica IV (2020),
lays out my hypothesized three epochs of the universe:
1) Infinite Potential is positioned front & center in Epoch I;
2) Planck's Quantum Mechanics - which I posit as metaphysical - is
   positioned front & center in Epoch II;
3) Our current (post-Big Bang) epoch - Epoch III - is a more complex
   Physical-Metaphysical hybrid (see the chronology).

* see www.Einstein1000.com

the theory is operative across time & space:

pre-Big Bang + catalyst of Big Bang + post-Big Bang

*"All that was new in the work, was false,
and all that was true, was old"*

– May 1859
   sample / negative initial academic reaction
   by Professor Samuel Haughton
   of Dublin, Ireland
   to Charles Darwin's newly-published
   Origin of Species

'the Common Denominator of 14 billion years of cosmic history/evolvement...'

'Complexification (C+) gets us from a single-cell organism ~4 billion years ago > to Beethoven'

Future Technology

Virginia Polytechnic Institute and State University in Blacksburg

Founded in 1872, Virginia Tech has the largest number of degree offerings in Virginia, more than 125 campus buildings, a 2,600-acre main campus, off-campus educational facilities in six regions, a study-abroad site in Switzerland, and a 1,700-acre agriculture research farm near the main campus.

January 5, 2015

Complexification (C+): Cornerstone of Summa Metaphysica's Potentialism Theory

By aaronphipps in Science Tags: Einstein, Theory

To physicist Albert Einstein - architect, Theory of Relativity 1905-1916 - everything is, of course, *relative*; however, to cosmologist/metaphysicist David Birnbaum - author/architect of Summa Metaphysica/Potentialism Theory 4 volumes 1988-2020, everything is, of course, *potential*. To Birnbaum who is *wrapping-around* Einstein, *Relativity* is nice for macro-physics, but to get one's arms around the entire cosmic order (super-macro-physics), one needs to work with a more overarching concept – Potential. See SummaMetaphysica.com.

Birnbaum likes Potential because he can play with the term and resolve virtually all the key questions in metaphysics and its related field of cosmology – with one quite-concise theme and formula.

What dynamic is eternal? Infinite Quest for Potential∞ [see Eternal1000.com]

What dynamic drives the Cosmic Order? Quest for Potential∞ [see theQ4P.com]

What is the purpose of Man? To reach his Potential [see ExaminerPurpose.com]

What is the end-goal of the cosmos? Infinite Potential realization [see Extraordinariation.com]

So, with minimal pivoting, Potential emerges as the ultimate 'plug' in metaphysics/cosmology.

And just where did this little dynamic come from? Birnbaum frontally addresses the issue:

By Definition, Potential/Possibility is eternal.

\# It is Self-evident that Potential/Possibility is eternal; there is, indeed a universe; thus, there must have been the Potential for it to exist.

Birnbaum believes that his little By Definition/Self-evident '1-2 punch' seals-the-deal that Potential/Possibility is eternal; he may just be right; and it's nice to solve a 7,000 year-old conundrum with a conceptual finesse.

Potentialism was discerned by metaphysicist and cosmologist David Birnbaum of Manhattan. Harvard and yeshiva-educated Birnbaum is an intellectual maverick; but he is a demanding and highly-disciplined intellectual warrior. In the 25+ years since the introduction of his Potentialism Theory (aka Quest for Potential$^{\infty}$ Theory aka Q4P-Theory) in Summa Metaphysica I by Ktav Publishing (NJ), no flaw has been discerned in the elegant theory.

Per Birnbaum, Infinite Quest for Potential drives the universe forward towards the super-extraordinary via its intermediate dynamic – Complexification. Notated C+, Complexification is a cornerstone of Potentialism theory. See Glossary1000.com.

The theory itself is laid-out in Birnbaum's three-part series:

Summa Metaphysica I: Religious Man: God and Evil (Ktav, 1988);

Summa Metaphysica II: Spiritual Man: God and Good (New Paradigm Matrix, 2005);

Summa Metaphysica III: Secular Man: The Transcendent Dynamic (New Paradigm Matrix, 2014).

See SummaMetaphysica.com.

In the series, Birnbaum explains that the universe is ruled by a central equation, $Q4P^{\infty} \rightarrow E+$. The formula dictates that the Infinite Quest for Potential$^{\infty}$ drives the universe towards an ultimate goal – of the super-extraordinary, or, in Birnbaum's lexicon, Extraordinariation (E+).

This E+ is the ultimate state of super-complexity on both a mechanical and metaphysical level – thus the greatest hypothetical level of super-complexity in all forms. E+ is actually a goal/horizon to be sought-after, but never quite realized. See Cosmic-Journey.com.

Driving the universe towards this E+ on a day-to-day basis is the cosmic workhorse, Potential's handmaiden, Birnbaum's hypothesized C+, or Complexification. This intermediate dynamic (in between Quest for Potential$^{\infty}$ and E+) is what advances and shapes and iterates the universe in ever-greater degrees of super-complexity.

To understand C+, it is necessary to distinguish it from mere complexity-advance. We must differentiate between the two terms inasmuch as while Summa Metaphysica I (1988) touched-upon Complexification (C+), contemporary (2014) cutting-edge physics (Seth Lloyd of MIT for example) now deploys complexity-advance as centerpiece in a mechanistic cosmological model. See Intermediate1000.com.

The simple issue is that complexity-advance does not get us to Extraordinariation (E+); however, Complexification (C+) does. See ParadigmChallenge.com.

Complexity-advance represents only incremental/linear advance in layers of complexity; C+ incorporates neo-quantum advances – via increased complexity, sophistication, richness, integration, diversity and wondrousness. Thus, plain vanilla complexity-advance is but one of multiple components of Complexification.

In any event, we now need to insert Complexification (C+) into the formula – and the theory's SuperLaw equation emerges:

$$Q4P^\infty > C+ > E+$$

It is sometimes easiest to juxtapose complexity-advance v. Complexification side by side to more clearly see understand the differences.

Complexity-advance v. Complexification (C+)

_____

linear v. qualitative advance
incremental v. neo-quantum advance
plain vanilla advance v. profound advance
active within relatively narrow parameters v. active within expandable parameters
narrow-spectrum v. wide-spectrum differentiation
mechanistic v. organic
physical v. metaphysical process
iterative v. iterative/evolving/morphing/quantum-step-up/dynamic process
closed v. open system
neo-Darwinian v. Birnbaumian
complexity-advance alone v. a package of advances (including complexity-advance)

Teleology (purpose/direction)

Unlike plain-vanilla complexity-advance, C+ is consonant with our teleological model. The Cosmic Order, and, in parallel, life on Earth, advances through intermittent neo-quantum jumps towards the ever more extraordinary. These are not simply direction-oriented linear/incremental advances; these are profound advances in the cosmic march towards E+.

The emergence of life, language, consciousness, and emotion, for example, simply cannot be labeled as purely linear advance. However, through C+, not only is the emergence of multi-cellular life from single-cell life better understood, but also aesthetics, love, music, art and morality.

Put another way, C+ in the equation explains the advance of Evolution; Complexity-advance alone does not.

Quantum Changes

C+ also helps describes advance in quantum terms. Complexity-advance is a well enough tool to describe day-to-day shifts. Complexity-advance gets us, if you will, incremental, linear change. But the truly quantum changes, those redefining moments in the nature of the universe, require C+ and a more profound shift in the nature of existence. When speaking of complexity, you may be able to isolate the differences between a hydrogen atom and a helium atom, but how does complexity describe the fundamental change that gave rise to the first molecule? This is where complexity-advance begins to be wholly inadequate. Not only that, but complexity-advance alone utterly fails when trying to describe any form of non-physical complexity.

More to the point, complexity-advance can only take us only so far in explaining natural selection and evolution. 'Plain vanilla' complexity-advance falls apart when trying to explain universe 'luxuries' such as music, art, humor, romance, altruism, spirituality et al. These 'luxury' aspects of the universe hardly seem to be 'survival traits'. Undeniably, these are all qualities we associate with the highest life forms we know of. So, it seems that the term complexity-advance has limitations and is simply incapable of capturing all that that is actually occurring.

the Common Denominator

Birnbaum re-iterates that a cosmological theory must be universal – and true on all levels, from the macro to micro and everything in between. Moreover, a cosmological theory must be as true for physical forms and matter as it is for concepts and ideals. Thus the evolution of thought, emotion and spirituality must advance just as the physical universe does. And it has. Just as the universe has grown from particles to atoms to molecules and stars (as a result of C+), so has consciousness grown from instinct to reason to art to morality and altruism (again as a direct result of C+). Complexification (C+) yields-us the Common Denominator of 14 billion years of cosmic history/evolvement. Complexity-advance does not. See SummaCoverage. com.

Getting to Beethoven

To encapsule the issue, Complexification gets us from a single-cell organism 4 billion years ago to Beethoven completing his 9th Symphony in 1624; Complexity-advance simply does not; the leaner dynamic simply does not have the 'firepower' – multi-dimensional breadth and depth – to catalyze the endless extraordinary morphings necessary to get us from a single-cell organism to Mr. Ludwig van Beethoven. See Beethoven1000.com.

Not as a stand-alone metaphysics

Complexification (C+) is a powerful dynamic; however, one should not be overly tempted in setting it up as a stand-alone metaphysics; it works as an intermediate dynamic, but fails as a stand-alone metaphysics. Why?

C+ has the 'tail-wind' of Quest for Potential breathing cosmic energy/chi into it from eternal origins, and is beckoned-forth by Extraordinariation (E+) at infinite horizon forward; C+ (conceptually and reality-wise) only 'works' when bracketed by these two infinite, Potential-suffused metaphysical bookends. See also TheoryCore.com.

In any event, more precisely, there is no clear divide between Q4P and C+; the two are interconnected

in any event.

Nuts & Bolts courtesy of MIT

Recent hi-level scientific/academic works offering the nuts & bolts for the mechanism of Complexification (first introduced by Birnbaum in 1988 via Summa Metaphysica I, Ktav) include the following: See also xMIT1000.com.

Programming the Universe (Knopf, 2006) by Professor of Quantum Mechanics Seth Lloyd of MIT (noted above, as Lloyd deploys 'complexity-advance' as centerpiece);

Our Mathematical Universe (Knopf, 2014) by Professor of Physics & Mathematics Max Tegmark of MIT.

Birnbaum had stood alone since Summa Metaphysica I in 1988 as a voice elucidating a matrix-like teleological universe; for almost two decades he had single-handedly faced-off across-the-board hostility from the apex predators in scientific academe; he was more than pleased to have 'the U.S. Cavalry' – in the form of Lloyd and Tegmark of MIT – 'charge to his rescue' in the 2006-2014 zone with their dovetailing metaphysics books; the two 'MIT books' complement each other – and each work offers a proposed scientific schema for a matrix-like teleological universe. Nice to have world class physicists Lloyd and Tegmark providing 'covering fire.'

Vindication via MIT is nice.

There is an order to our universe - on multiple levels.

Key
Pillars and Dynamics

[key inter-related hypotheses]

Key Pillars of Summa Theory	Introduced in Volume	Year
THE ETERNAL 'SOMETHING' POTENTIAL	I	1988
INFINITE QUEST FOR POTENTIAL$^{\infty}$ Q4P$^{\infty}$	I	1988
THE PINNACLE NATURAL DYNAMIC Q4P$^{\infty}$	I	1988
COSMIC WOMB OF POTENTIAL CWP	II	2005
COMPLEXIFICATION C+	II	2005
EXTRAORDINARIATION E+	II	2005
THE BIRNBAUM SUPER-FORMULA Q4P$^{\infty} \rightarrow$ C+$\rightarrow$ E+	II	2005
THE BIRNBAUM DIRECTION OF THE UNIVERSE Q4P$^{\infty} \rightarrow$ C+$\rightarrow$ E+	II	2005
		>>>

MACRO-HOLISTIC-OPTIMIZATION $Q4P^\infty \rightarrow C+ \rightarrow E+$	II	2005
THE 'GOD FORMULA' (PINNACLE NATURAL DYNAMIC) $Q4P^\infty \rightarrow C+ \rightarrow E+$	II	2005
THE ESSENCE OF THE RANDOM HUMAN $Q4P^\infty \rightarrow C+ \rightarrow E+$	II	2005
THE BIRNBAUM EVOLUTION SHORTHAND $Q4P^\infty \rightarrow C+ \rightarrow E+$	III	2014
3 EPOCHS	IV	2020
# BACKWARD CAUSATION # LEVERAGED-BUYOUT # THE 'ORIGINAL PULSE'	IV	2020
# THE VOID COULDN'T 'TAKE IT' ANYMORE # SPLITTING METAPHYSICAL ZERO	IV	2020

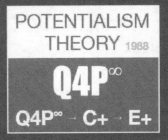

see www.David1000.com   academic overview

David Birnbaum / Summa Metaphysica

QUICK-TOUR

Summa Metaphysica proposes
an original and elegant metaphysics

FOCUS

Summa goes for the crux of the matter: It endeavors to discern the fount and engine of the cosmic order.

The author's conclusion is simple yet complex: Quest for Potential∞

Summa Metaphysica discerns this one unifying concept. The author proposes that this one dynamic – is eternal, transcending, and overarching.

The author makes-the-case that it is *self-evident* that the only dynamic which can be asserted with full conviction as being truly eternal is Potential/Possibility. By definition.

The religious finesse would be that Holy Quest for Potential is eternal.

On Summa's ambitious to-do list is the quasi-unification – via the universal common core axis of Potential∞ – of Science, Religion and Philosophy.

As we are aware, however, establishments do not readily yield to paradigm shifts – without a battle.

New Paradigm Matrix™

"in some manner ...life, mind, and physical law are

part of a common scheme, mutually supporting"

Paradigm Shift Possible ?

DAVIES

on Cosmology

excerpts from
Paul Davies*

"A deeper level of explanation" ?

"I belong to the group of scientists who do not subscribe to a conventional religion but nevertheless deny that the universe is purposeless accident. Through my scientific work I have come to believe more and more strongly that the physical universe is put together with an ingenuity so astonishing that I cannot accept it merely as a brute fact. There must, it seems to me, be a deeper level of explanation"....

– from *The Mind of God, p. 16*
Simon & Schuster, © 1992

"...Somehow the universe has engineered, not just its own awareness, but also its own comprehension. Mindless, blundering atoms have conspired to make not just life, not just mind, but understanding.... Could it just be a fluke? Might the fact that the deepest level of reality has connected to a quirky natural phenomenon we call 'the human mind' represent nothing but a bizarre and temporary aberration in an absurd and pointless universe? Or is there an even deeper subplot at work?"...

"In some manner...life, mind, and physical law are part of a common scheme, mutually supporting. Somehow, the universe has engineered its own self-awareness."...

– from *The Goldilocks Enigma, pp. 5 and 231*
Little, First Mariner Books, © 2008

*Paul Davies has been a recipient of the following awards/prizes: 1995 Templeton Prize (US); Advance Australia Award and two Eureka Prizes (Australia); 2001 Kelvin Medal and Prize by the Institute of Physics, and the 2002 Faraday Prize by The Royal Society (UK)

EXCERPTS ONLY / NOT A TESTIMONIAL

see also Paul Davies Video
15 min / August 2019

"the Quest for Potential Theory challenges for the throne"

NEWS   SPORT ▾   BLOGS   UK COMMUNITY   GLOBAL COMMUNITY ▾   TRAVEL   MOVE TO ▾   VIDEOS

Has Outsider David Birnbaum Trumped the Entire Academic Establishment?

Posted on November 9, 2014 *by* Candice McMillan in NEWS

The Quest for Potential Theory challenges for the throne.

David Birnbaum (see David1000. com) of Manhattan is a yeshiva-educated and Harvard educated independent scholar. His multi-decade 'night job' focus has been metaphysics – the origins and purpose of the cosmic order. To this end, over the years he has crafted a three-part treatise Summa Metaphysica; the extraordinary treatise delineates Birnbaum's original and elegant Potentialism Theory.

Birnbaum first focuses on cosmic origins: What ignited the Cosmic Order? As is known, the world's greatest thinkers and scientists have been stymied here. The list of luminaries, who have tried and failed on this score, is a long one; Socrates, Plato and Aristotle lead-off the list (see ExaminerPurpose.com). Intellectual maverick David Birnbaum was undeterred. His Theory of Potential now challenges for the pinnacle in the pantheon of ideas on this subject.

Birnbaum's Quest for Potential Theory proposes that there is indeed a protagonist to the cosmic order, but that the protagonist is a 'quest,' and not an entity. According to the theory, the universe quests for its maximal potential. Birnbaum's proposed core dynamic, Quest for Potential∞ strives with purpose towards ever-greater and richer potential (see TheoryCore.com). As individuals, man and woman seek his or her individual potential, so too do the cosmic order as a whole. Birnbaum delineates a pure and powerful scientific theory of design and purpose pivoting off of this one theme of potential. (See also TheQ4P.com).

At the 'beginning of time', according to Birnbaum's hypothesis, eternal Quest for Potential∞ harnessed the eternal equations of Physics-Mathematics to ignite our universe via the Big Bang (see ParadigmChallenge.com). This same symbiotic dynamic – Quest for Potential∞ in league with Physics-Math, then acted as a catalyst for life, evolution, language, emotion, consciousness, and, indeed, for all the dynamics which have evolved in the universe.

The theory (see PotentialismTheory.com) is stunning in its relative simplicity and conciseness. It almost seems too good to be true. However since first proposed by David Birnbaum in 1988, no flaw has been found in it – and high-level academics and clergy globally have praised it. In the meanwhile, over a dozen colleges – including UCLA, Brandeis and Hebrew University (Jerusalem) have assigned it as a Course Text. Bard College (Upstate NY) whose motto is 'a place to think' hosted a major 3 ½ day international academic conference (see Bard1000.com) focused on the work's unification of Science and Religion. Over two dozen journals have featured Birnbaum's Summa Metaphysica and its Theory of Potential (see SummaCoverage.com).

Birnbaum's Quest for Potential theory seeks to dethrone the reigning academic theory of choice – Randomness/atheism. According to this entrenched academic theory, there is no order or design whatsoever to the universe; it is all random happenstance: The Big Bang, the billions of galaxies and their trillions of stars, life, humans, evolution, consciousness are all random occurrences which just so happened to dovetail in our little universe. There is no design or direction to the universe. Contemporary British philosophers swear by it. Birnbaum frontally challenges it.

Birnbaum's Quest for Potential theory provides a 'big tent' embracing all who might see some design or spirituality or direction to the universe, hence the three typologies in his three volume titles: Religious, Spiritual and Secular Man. These typologies embrace around 99 percent of the planet. But even Birnbaum's three typologies do not embrace the one percent of the planet which is hard-line atheistic, which rejects any possibility whatsoever of design or direction or purpose to the universe. As fate would have it, this one percent somehow gained hegemony in Britain's elite universities which disproportionately control the top academic journals, hence the stand-off. See HuffPost2Scemas.com.

The 'insider' professorial atheist group is not happy with 'outsider' Birnbaum trying to beat them at their own game – and apparently prevailing. Rumor has it that the insider professorial atheist group wants to cut off some of his vital body parts. To-date, Birnbaum has adroitly parried all attacks; his own global academic counterattack has been formidable.

A global battle for the soul of metaphysics has ensued: Birnbaum's Potentialism v. Atheism's Randomnness. One guy against 1000. David v. Goliath? Stay tuned.

Potentialism Theory: The Summa series

Summa Metaphysica I: Religious Man: God and Evil (Ktav, November 1988);
Summa Metaphysica II: Spiritual Man: God and Good (New Paradigm Matrix, March 2005);
Summa Metaphysica III: Secular Man: The Transcendent Dynamic (New Paradigm Matrix, January 2014). See SummaMetaphysica.com.

Potentialism Theory: Dovetailing: MIT & NYU

Recent hi-level academic works dovetailing with Birnbaum's Theory of Potential – and essentially vindicating his core thrust – include the following:

Programming the Universe (Knopf, 2006) by Professor of Quantum Mechanics Seth Lloyd of MIT;
Mind & Cosmos (Oxford Press, 2012) by Professor of Philosophy & Law Thomas Nagel of NYU;
Our Mathematical Universe (Knopf, 2014) by Professor of Physics Max Tegmark of MIT.

Fantasy?

Fantasy. All revolutions are considered [fantasy] - until they happen; then they are [solemnly deemed] historical inevitabilities.

DAVID MITCHELL, Cloud Atlas

MORPHED COSMIC ORDER

Section K

MORPHED COSMIC ORDER

SUIS GENERIS

POTENTIALISM THEORY

ORIGINAL / POWERFUL / SEAMLESS

Q4P$^\infty$ is optimizing & iterating

POTENTIALISM THEORY

It 'ignited' the Big Bang; tweaks the genomes ongoing to advance Evolution; and drives our universe forward

---

*"it is reasonable to propose the Quest for Potential$^\infty$ as a **working hypothesis** for exploring the impetus behind the cosmic dynamic"*

POTENTIALISM THEORY

- Prof. Andrei Alyokhin,
Ecology & Biology chief at Univ of Maine

---

he (hitherto elusive) ARROW OF TIME

POTENTIALISM THEORY

Q4P$^\infty$ > C+ > E+

'hiding in plain sight'

POTENTIALISM THEORY

the (hitherto elusive)
Metaphysics of the Cosmic Order

MORPHED COSMIC ORDER

"a powerful hybrid construct - Potentialism/Quantum Universe

which readily trumps Randomness..."

world.edu
global education network

How Harvard and MIT checkmated Oxford and Cambridge

Posted on September 16, 2014 *by* guest

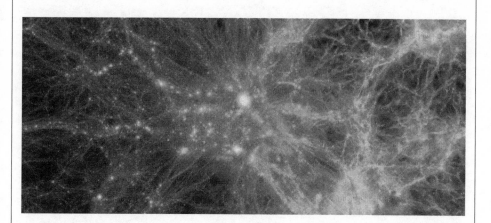

Oxford and Cambridge have long been the gatekeepers of modern cosmology. Indeed, in recent decades they have ruthlessly protected their power over academe; while suppressing any challenging theories, they have touted their Randomness/Atheism construct as the only plausible theory of cosmic origins.

Randomness/Atheism posits that the universe is random, devoid of purpose and inexorably decaying and falling apart. Their theory can be summarized in one simple and easy-to-remember phrase: All is random.

Coming into the 21st century challengers to this antiquated theory include Harvard-educated David Birnbaum and MIT's Seth Lloyd. Their respective constructs dovetail with each other's. Coming from the metaphysics and physics arenas respectively, Birnbaum and Lloyd de facto offer a powerful hybrid construct – Potentialism/Quantum Universe which readily trumps Randomness/Atheism theory.

David Birnbaum is an independent metaphysicist and author of the widely-featured Summa Metaphysica series – Summa Metaphysica I, II and III (Ktav, 1988; New Paradigm Matrix, 2005; and New Paradigm Matrix, 2014). Seth Lloyd is a professor of Quantum Mechanics and Mechanical Engineering at MIT, and the author of Programming the Universe (Knopf, 2006).

In 1988, Birnbaum proposed an audacious theory of the universe in his Summa Metaphysica I. What if the universe isn't purposeless? What if, completely contrary to the entrenched academic/scientific dogma, it was the exact opposite? What Birnbaum proposed, was his profound and powerful Theory of Potential (see SummaCoverage.com).

The theory proposes – concisely capturing cosmic history in one simple phrase – that the universe strives towards its optimal potential. And the theory does more than just describe the natural world; it describes the universe in its entirety – from macro to micro levels, with humanity somewhere in the middle. Language, emotion, and beauty are, of course, included in-the-mix.

The Birnbaum theory basically discerns a Common Denominator – infinite divine quest for potential – to the entire cosmic order. As noted, this cosmic Common Denominator operates across the entire spectrum of universe-levels. The universe is not a mish-mash of aimlessness and decay, as per the Randomness/Atheistic crew; rather it is purpose-driven integrated organic entity seeking advance and growth.

Advance and growth – these are things the Randomness/Atheistic crew will never likely understand. But the truth is, if Randomness/Atheism can't account for the way the universe manifests, then it is a fatally flawed theory. By comparison, Birnbaum tackles all these issues head on. Potentialism describes human emotion and art as easily as it describes thermodynamics and gravity. Everything in the universe is describable in terms of Potential. And the theory seamlessly handles the entire flow of cosmic history and advance.

For those who wonder where the hard math of science comes in, that is where Seth Lloyd enters the story. Lloyd has done extensive research on quantum mechanics and how it shapes the natural world around us. Based on his extensive knowledge, Lloyd has also produced highly respected computer century though, the US has unleashed two sophisticated and cutting-edge models of how the universe is governed by quantum mechanical principles.

And what are MIT Professor Seth Lloyd's own findings? Lloyd in his 2006 work *Programming the Universe* sees the universe as a quantum information-processing organic entity. That's a mouthful, but what Lloyd is proposing is that the universe keeps iterating and advancing to seek ever-richer complexity. But wait, that is what Birnbaum first proposed in 1988 (see SummaMetaphysica.com).

In any event, the 2006 Lloyd theory complements – and dovetails with – the 1988 Birnbaum theory. Birnbaum's Theory of Potential actually wraps-around the (more limited and contained) Lloyd proposition. Birnbaum in 1988 provides the conceptual context, concept, igniter, drive and goal of the universe; Lloyd proposes the (crucial) mechanics; Birnbaum has been clear – see www. ParadigmChallenge.com – that he is quite honored to have MIT's Lloyd as part of his metaphysics/physics tag-team; together, they present an elegant 21st growth and advance, quite readily trumping the (now antiquated) 20th construct of decay and aimlessness.

The advance of knowledge and science is inexorable; Harvard's Birnbaum and MIT's Lloyd have successfully dethroned Cambridge and Oxford's hegemony, and set-the-stage for 21st cosmology. Onward!

Summa Metaphysica

Cosmic Tool Kit
Overview

Shelf #1

tools:

* DIVISION INTO POLARITIES &
  DUALITIES *

* SIMULTANEOUS PUSH / PULL
  TENSION *

* INFINITELY-COILED SPIRALITY *

* COSMIC 'LEVERAGED BUYOUT'
  ("BOOTSTRAPPING") *

* (INFINITE) RECURSIVENESS &
  (INFINITE) LOOP-ABILITY *

* 1:1 METAPHYSICAL
  CORRESPONDENCE *

* MITOSIS OF "0" *

* INEXORABLE LIFE-QUESTING *

* VACUUM-BUSTING *

* INEXORABLE & INFINITE ASCENTS *

* MULTI-DIMENSIONAL MORPHING *

* OPTIMIZATION *

* COSMIC-TAPESTRY-WEAVING *

* QUEST FOR INFINITE DIVINE
  EXTRAORDINARIATION *

* INTERLOCKING DIVINE INFINITUDE
  QUEST *

* HYPER-COSMIC
  RESOURCEFULNESS *

Shelf #2

tools:

* SUBJECTIVITY OF "INFINITE
  DIVINE EXTRAORDINARIATION" *

* HYPER-ITERATION *

* SIMULTANEOUS OPERATION
  LEVELS *

* ONE ORGANIC SUPER-EQUATION *

* INSTINCT-DNA *

* RECURSIVITY IS REGNANT
  (RECURSIVITY REIGNS) *

* EXTRAORDINARIATION *

* EMOTION-EXPRESSION-DRAMA *

* OPTIMIZING
  COMPLEXIFICATION /
  CONTOURIZATION *

* MACRO-HOLISTIC-OPTIMIZATION *

* CHERRY-PICKED EVOLUTION *

* TEMPLATE FIDELITY *

* METAPHYSICAL > PHYSICAL
  LEVERAGED BUYOUT *

* CUMULATIVE / MASSED-ARRAY
  DESIGN *

a unified and overarching

universal *Common Denominator* hypothesis

Metaphysics → Cosmology → Evolution

Summa Metaphysica:
The (true) Theory of Everything

By Ron Moran | June 11, 2014

In 1988, metaphysicist David Birnbaum entered the arena of cosmology with the release of his book Summa Metaphysica I. Challenging the atheist dogma of Randomness Theory, Birnbaum proposed his competing Theory of Potentialism (see ExaminerPurpose.com). In doing so, he not only split with traditional, mainstream cosmological theory, but further upped the ante by offering an audacious solution to the most universally elusive problem of physics and cosmology alike: The Theory of Everything.

The Theory of Everything (ToE) has long been the holy grail of physicists, cosmologists and philosophers and science as a whole. For physicists, the quest has always been for Unifying Theory – the physical/mathematical model which would illustrate the relationship between the micro (quantum physics) and the macro (Newtonian physics and relativity). For cosmologists, metaphysicists and philosophers, the quest has been even broader – their ultimate answer would go beyond Unifying Theory to incorporate into the explanation thought and existence as well – The Theory of Everything.

While this might sound like a punch line from a Douglas Adams novel, the Theory of Everything is serious business to cosmologists, particularly metaphysicists and philosophers. People less familiar with metaphysics might find it curious that such an unabashed metaphysicist as Birnbaum would be brave enough to step into the ring with physicists. Metaphysics is often times incorrectly associated with ghost hunters or crystal collecting, new age mystics. For the record, this is a gross misunderstanding of an established branch of science.

Metaphysics straddles the line between physics (and more broadly – empirical science), and classical philosophy. Metaphysics is, properly: the branch of philosophy concerned with the fundamental nature of reality that includes ontology, cosmology and epistemology. It is no accident cosmology lies squarely within the realm of philosophy. Why is that?

Quite simply, the "hard" sciences, such as physics, rely on the process of gathering empirical evidence and applying deductive logic to formulate a conclusion. While this is a wonderful tool for science, it has one limitation – it cannot be used in an open system. This isn't usually an issue in science. One can apply boundaries to create a closed system to study. However, cosmology deals with the universe as a whole. And by universe, that means everything. The universe, by definition, has no "outside" the system – or we're no longer talking about the universe.

For cosmology, at some point someone has to step forward and make assumptions and that is simply something a philosopher is far more comfortable doing than a physicist. Formally, we call these assumed truths axioms – a very scientific word, but basically jargon for "informed hunch". That is not to say anyone gets a free pass from scientific rigor. An axiom needs to stand up to inductive scrutiny. Unlike a deductive conclusion, an inductive conclusion's strength is measured by the amount of supporting evidence it has.

If this still sounds dubious, it might serve to remember that mathematics is part of the formal sciences (a by-product of philosophy, if you will) as opposed to physics, which resides in the physical sciences. If you're using mathematics, or the scientific method for that matter, then you're engaged squarely in philosophy. So have no doubt, metaphysicists belong squarely in the debate on the nature of the universe, likely more so than their instrument carrying physicist cousins – though the true pioneers of cosmology and science tend to be adept at both disciplines. As Einstein famously said, "Nature is the realization of the simplest conceivable mathematical ideas. ... I am convinced that we can discover by means of purely mathematical constructions the concepts and the laws connecting them with each other."

That is exactly what Birnbaum has set out to do with the Theory of Potentialism – identify the structure and nature of the cosmos and, in so doing, seek out the elusive Theory of Everything. For the necessarily inductive test of Potentialism, there are some criteria it must meet for a solid Theory: It must be pervasive in both scale and breadth. It must be valid on both the micro and macro scale. It also must be demonstrable over the breadth of the cosmos – that is, it must be demonstrably valid across the fields of biology, physics, chemistry... in short, universal. Further, to fully encompass ToE from the metaphysical perspective, it must be ontologically inclusive – that is, it must incorporate the nature of being itself. 'How everything is' is not sufficient. The metaphysical Theory of Everything demands the why of being as well.

Summa Metaphysica: The Quest for Infinite Potential

Potentialism's central mechanic is the Quest for Infinite Potential. Logically, it is expressed as $Q4P\infty{\rightarrow}E+$. Don't let the nomenclature fool you. It's simply a concise, logical expression of the Theory. Like any new branch of thought or mathematics or science, it comes with its own logical expressions.

On a most basic level, Potentialism identifies inferentially the Quest for Infinite Potential as the prime mover of cosmology. The Q4P axiom states that the universe is in such a state as to naturally be driven towards infinite complexity – infinite in this sense being that there is no state of rest, or sufficient complexity, in this system – rather it is a continual and endless process.

That being said, while the universe is constantly and visibly changing, those changes are not usually profound. Rather, in a quantum sense, the universe continually increases in Potentiality towards the complex, towards transitive moments which Potentialists identify as Extraordinariation – pivotal moments of change in universal complexity.

The concept is easily grasped in terms of the universe's evolution on an astrophysical scale. At the very beginning of the universe when the singularity that was our perceivable universe exploded in a "Big Bang", the universe reached a critical state of change abruptly and began to spread. Likewise, the formation of the first hydrogen atoms is considered a cosmic moment of Extraordinariation (see Extraordinariation.com).

Potentialism Theory states that the universe eternally, by virtue of its natural Potential, builds towards these moments of Extraordinariation that invariably leave the universe in a more complex state than it was in previously. Looking strictly from an astrophysical perspective, it's fairly obvious this is an inferentially sound axiom. But the true test is whether Potentialism Theory is universally applicable to broader natural and philosophical phenomena if it is to stand as a viable Theory of Everything (see PotentialismTheory.com).

Summa Metaphysica: Unifying Science, Spirituality and Philosophy

One of the greatest shortcomings of cosmological theory is trying to understand the universe scientifically, philosophically and spiritually. It's bad enough trying to merge abstract philosophical concepts with the scientific ones, but trying to merge the spiritual as well has usually been catastrophic. This has left people forced to analyze cosmology through different filters. You can speak about the Big Bang through a scientific filter, leaving the spiritual and philosophical questions of existence behind. Likewise, you can simply regard the universe from a spiritual or philosophical perspective. But, like quantum mechanics and Newtonian physics, these filters don't play nicely together in the same sandbox.

For proponents of Potentialism, this is one of the greatest achievements of Potentialist Theory. Potentialism provides a common ground of understanding where one doesn't have to play scientist by day, philosopher by night and spiritualist with their congregation. We mentioned astrophysics before, but you'll find Q4P works just as neatly as a descriptor of evolution. Those transitive E+ moments of Extraordinariation? Describing the ascendancy of multi-cellular life, the first animals to walk instead of swim, even the rise of humankind all fit just as well into the logical model of Q4P as the birth of atoms and molecules do. It's one of the innate strengths of Potentialism to oftentimes leave someone slapping their heads at the obvious simplicity of the Theory and how well it is applied equally to different universal phenomena.

But where does this leave spirituality? Interestingly, the answer resides in the nature of Q4P. If Q4P is a universal "prime mover", the source of the Big Bang and what has driven the creation of stars and humankind alike since that time, then there is something beyond just matter and energy and void – Potential itself. You can see where this is headed. But to be clear, Potentialism does not address directly the existence or the nature of the divine. Potentialism is science, not religion. But, for the religious or spiritual, Potentialism offers acceptance and reserves a place for them.

Potentialism does recognize, given the universal nature of Q4P, the natural existence of teleological systems. A teleological system simply means it is purpose driven. It's not nearly as mystical as it sounds. It is just a formal way of stating what we've been seeing all along – if Q4P is pushing the universe towards increased complexity than the universe is, by definition, changing with a purpose (see ParadigmChallenge.com).

It's the nature of this prime mover that leaves room for atheist and religious alike. To the atheist – yes, there is a universal drive of creation, but it need not be a named, bearded man who carves legal code on stone tablets. To the atheist, they may simply look on Q4P as an inherent force in the universe, no more mystical than physics or chemistry – just another rule and nothing more.

By contrast, there is nothing in Potentialism that is in conflict with an intelligent prime mover. You would think this might leave the religious a bit put out, but that is where we step into the realm of spirituality. To the spiritualist, any concrete, irrefutable evidence of the divine is impossible. It creates this untenable paradox: Religion requires faith and faith requires uncertainty. To prove God's existence would disprove it. A bizarre concept to the non-philosophers reading this, but this is generally accepted as fact by most religious philosophers. So, the atheist can be comfortable that there is some force of nature at work that doesn't require classic intelligence, while the religious can be comfortable that the Alpha and Omega exists and they will have faith in its intelligence in whatever form they believe.

Summa Metaphysica: Unifying Micro and Macro Physics

The second big test for Potentialism is that Unifying Theory we previously alluded to. What's true on the micro level should be true on the macro level. There are three points to make on this subject. Firstly, micro and macro physics follow the same rules of Q4P and resultant Extraordinariation. Secondly, there is a difference in the rules between micro and macro physics. Thirdly, it's okay. We'll get to that third one in a bit. First though, a brief look at the similarities between the micro and macro levels of physics.

If Q4P is to hold its soundness we would expect to see transitive moments in complexity at both the micro and macro scales. On a micro level, in the first moment after the Big Bang, there were simply particles. We won't over-dwell on the weirdness of the hadron epoch and other epochs in the first seconds, just suffice it to say there were a lot of little particles having their brief eras in the first fraction of a second. But jumping ahead to the first roughly 3.2 minutes after the Big Bang, we have nucleosynthesis where protons and neutrons begin to combine – again, one of those transitive moments where Potential gives rise to Extraordinariation. These moments continue cyclically as the basic elements begin to form and, yet again, when the elements begin to bond into molecular structures.

Likewise, this Q4P to Extraordinariation is visible on the macro scale of universal history as the primitive plasma cloud of the very early universe, to the matter domination era of 300,000 years after the Big Bang, to 300 million years after the Big Bang when stars and galaxies began to form. It is clear to see, not only the continual evolution of the cosmos towards greater complexity but the distinctive stages of complexity predicted by Q4P when Extraordinariation events occurred.

But what of Unifying Theory? While we've seen that the micro and macro do show clear similarities in how Q4P structures their evolution, there are still vast differences between quantum and Newtonian physics. Why do quantum events tend to follow a binary (on/off) model? Why do Newtonian events tend to follow analogue/wave patterns? Why does gravity not interact on a quantum level like it does on massive scales?

Part of the key is to look backwards through the Extraordinariation events to simpler epochs. Potentialism posits that physical laws had to have a simpler form in an earlier universe. That the fields of physics would diversify and become distinct, with their own governing laws, is actually predicted by Q4P. Hence, when we said it was alright. Just a year ago, physicists would have tossed such an absurd idea off as bunk or a flimsy excuse for science. But times change - and sometimes rapidly. We've only just this year detected quantum gravity waves in the cosmic background radiation. Why is this important and what does this have to do with Unifying Theory? "Quantum" and "Gravity" were just used in the same sentence.

For those without a pony in the game, one of the biggest problems in Unifying Theory is trying to explain gravity. To digress briefly, Einstein discovered quantum physics quite by accident. When he was formulating Relativity, Einstein found it too difficult to include Newtonian physics (which deals with gravity) into his Theory of Relativity. So, he left it out. Relativity was designed in this fictitious universe where gravity didn't exist and he called it the Theory of Special Relativity. A curious aside to this was the discovery of quantum mechanics. But, at the time, Einstein thought little of it because – again – this was a hypothetical universe. Later he incorporated gravity and that became his General Theory of Relativity.

What was not expected was that quantum mechanics really did exist in the General Relativity universe. Yet, quantum mechanics was only supposed to work right in a flat universe. And gravity warps and bends time-space. This is the root of the conundrum. How to unify something that seemingly has no room for gravity with a universe that clearly does have gravity on a macro scale. To unify the micro and macro, there would have to be some presence of gravitational interaction on a micro level.

Flash forward back to current time and the cosmic background radiation. It would appear at first glance, we've finally been able to witness this elusive interaction as gravitational waves have polarized light from this radiation reaching us from near the very beginning of the universe. This tells us that, if confirmed, the micro and macro once interacted more homogeneously. But at some point in the very early stages of the universe, science crossed a threshold and the complexity of these two sciences increased – what we'd call simply an Extraordinariation event.

Summa Metaphysica: Unifying Math and Cosmology

A core principle of Potentialism is its infinitely nested nature. The strength of Q4P as a catalyst relies on its iterative, exponential nature. Think of it like a seed. A seed has the potential for a plant. But the resultant plant can also produce seeds to an entire generation of plants beyond that. So, within that one seed is an infinitely nested series of potentials. This is, by far, a gross simplification of Potentialism – but it suffices as an introduction to the principle. In short, for this to hold true to Potentialists, there should be an abundance, in the natural world, of observable phenomena which display infinite nesting and recursion.

On a mathematical level, this is exhibited by fractal mathematics and integral calculus. For those who think calculus looks like Greek Mad Libs – don't worry, we're not going to inundate you here with equations. What's important is the theory, not the actual grunt work of the equations. Integral calculus is commonly used for area calculations. What makes integral calculus so cool and unique is its ability to calculate areas that are infinitely irregular. Think of it like trying to calculate how deep a pool is in weather that leaves the surface rough. You can ballpark where the top is between waves, but its not exact. Integral calculus gives us a way of determining an area of such a surface not precisely, but infinitely close to precisely. It's so close to precisely so that the difference doesn't matter as it is infinitely small. Interesting side note: this "infinitely close to a number" means there are three zeros in calculus – 0+, 0, and 0-. What's the difference between 0+ and 0? You can't divide by 0 (see ZeroPointPortal.com). There's something to ponder over coffee.

While integral calculus deals with infinities, fractal mathematics deals with the infinitely nested. While you're still processing positive zero, here's another fun mathematical fact to ponder: Let's envision a fractal snowflake. A fractal has an infinitely nested complexity to its geometry. Know matter how small a scale you view it in, you'll always find another angle around the corner. How much of a fractal is a straight line? 0. How long, that is, what is the perimeter of our snowflake? Infinite. While it may encompass a finite amount of area, the fractal itself has an infinite length. No matter what detail you look at it in, you'll just find more and more jagged edges nested within each other.

As you can see, the concept of infinite and infinitely nested passes the test easily for Potentialists when looked at purely mathematically. But formal math isn't natural math. The real test is cosmological. Do these patterns exist pervasively in the real world? In short, yes. Let's look for the infinitely complex in both design and in regards to nesting.

Objects in the world, at every scale, display a naturally infinite complexity in mathematical design. Even a simple leaf follows fractal geometry in its design. It's not a true fractal, granted. That is, if you look at it under a microscope, you won't find tiny versions of the leaf pattern in every spike. But you can find plenty of examples which do so to a few orders of magnitude. But further, there are no naturally occurring straight lines or smooth surfaces in existence. The more you magnify an object, the more irregularities you find. Down at the atomic level you find constantly shifting electrons that preclude anything approaching even a real, solid surface – just wide open space with electrons winking in and out of different spaces, at seeming random, within a predefined space.

More important though (certainly to Potentialism) are the naturally occurring nested complexities that permeate the cosmos. Electrons orbit nuclei, planets orbit suns, stars orbit a galactic core. To Potentialists, there is little random about the universe. Yes, there's some probability involved in exactly where an electron might be around a nuclei or a star might be around a galaxy, but randomness it isn't. Only a fool would fail to see the clear patterns all around them. To the Potentialist, the inherent concepts of infinite and iterative infinite complexities in both formal mathematics as well as physical science are just two more pieces in a sea of evidence for inductively proving Q4P.

Summa Metaphysica: The Common Denominator and the Catalyst

Potentialist theory is just that – theory. But I'd humbly remind the reader of how many sciences share the suffix of "theory": Special Relativity Theory, Quantum Mechanical Theory, Field Theory, Grand Unification Theory.... I could do this all day. The point is that Theory is how we move forward and evolve our understanding of the universe. And in cosmology, solid inductive reasoning is the name of the game. Potentialism offers a viable understanding of the cosmos that can build bridges, not just between the sciences, but between beliefs as well – unifying not only the micro and macro, but the scientific, the philosophical and even the spiritual under a definition of one uniting concept, both Common Denominator and Catalyst. If something as simple as $Q4P\infty \rightarrow E+$ gives you pause, just remember what people thought one hundred years ago when they first saw something as simplistic as $E=mc^2$. Small equations can bring big change.

Summa Metaphysica: Context

Birnbaum elucidates his theory via his iconic 3-part treatise Summa Metaphysica (see SummaMetaphysica.com): Volume I: Religious Man (Ktav, 1988), Volume II: Spiritual Man (New Paradigm Matrix, 2005) and Volume III: Secular Man (New Paradigm Matrix, 2014). Over a dozen colleges globally including UCLA, Brandeis and Hebrew University (Jerusalem) have assigned the landmark work as a Course Text (see SummaCourseText.com).

Bard College (Upstate NY) hosted a 3 ½ day international academic conference in April 2012 on Science & Religion with the Summa treatise as its prime focus (see Conference1000.com). Over 30 feature articles globally have focused on Birnbaum's Summa Metaphysica and its Theory of Potential in the past twelve months alone (see SummaCoverage.com).

www.TToE1000.com

Does the Glove Fit?

*"If it doesn't fit,
        you must acquit"*

- Defense Attorney Johnnie Cochran 6/9/14
on behalf of O.J. Simpson
(at the riveting Simpson murder trial)

BUT,
in our discussion realm of metaphysics

if the **GLOVE** (Potentialism Theory)
does, indeed, apparently **FIT** (all the facts)
(i.e. all the trillions of *bona fide* truly established facts)

THEN

might you just have a
very serious ***Working Hypothesis***

- for a genuine Theory of Everything...

> *All revolutions are bloody*
>
> — Birnbaum

the   last   Greek   philosopher

CNN | Home | TV & Video | CNN Trends | U.S. | World | Politics | Justice | Entertainment | Tech | Health | Living | Travel | Opinion | iRepo

BREAKING NEWS | Russia gives ultimatum to Ukrainian forces in Crimea: Clear ou 11 hours or face 'military storm,' Russian state media report.

CNN iReport

🏠 Main   🔍 Explore   ✓ Assignments   👤 Prof

The Last Greek Philosopher

By ron1980 | Posted December 10, 2014

David Birnbaum, author of Summa Metaphysica

Progenitor of classic-modern hybrid 'Potentialism Theory'

He defines the 'cutting-edge 21st Century cosmologist; his original cosmological concepts have almost single-handedly overthrown 100+ year-old (British-centric) Randomness/Atheism theory; he melds Quantum Field Theory with General Relativity

Theory; he is the progenitor of conceptual breakthrough and paradigm-changing Potentialism Theory.

But is Manhattanite David Birnbaum not, more accurately, indeed, 'the Last Greek philosopher'?

Birnbaum may have been born in the 20th century and may have authored one of, if not the only, defining cosmological theories of the 21st century – but does conceptual theorist David Birnbaum arguably not have more in common with Aristotle than any of his 21st Century contemporaries? Dusting off such theories of antiquity as teleology and then arming them with original conceptualization, modern science and mathematics – Birnbaum has re-defined the field; like a Persian scholar in the Middle Ages, Birnbaum has become not only a protector of the wisdom of a past era, but also the consummate practitioner of inductive reasoning (see https://www.summametaphysica.com/harvardinductive/) – originally made famous by Aristotle et al.

Indeed, Birnbaum maintains that if the Greeks could be beamed-up (a la' Star Trek) to the 21st Century to read his works, they would sign on to his theory – and help him do battle with the rrear-guard gambits of the reactionary British Randomness/Atheists. Birnbaum views the classic Greek philosophers as his natural intellectual allies; loyal to conceptual elegance and empirical observation, and not inhibited by the limitations of laboratory experiment.

In his three-part metaphysics/cosmology/philosophy treatise – Summa Metaphysica – David Birnbaum has set course to for a revolutionary re-writing of the rules of metaphysics, cosmology and philosophy, he has dug deep into classical philosophy to separate myth from insight; superstition from science; and the past from the future.

Potentialism Theory, at its core, revolves around just a few simple, albeit radically new, concepts and equations: (See also Glossary1000.com.)

Q4P∞ – This is the infinite Quest for Potential∞ – the (overarching natural force) prime mover of the universe. It is an inherent drive in everything that exists to seek out new levels of Complexity.

C+ On the intermediate level, infinite potential inherently strives towards greater and greater levels of what Birnbaum coins as Complexification (shorthand: C+) the drive for ever-greater complexity/sophistication/richness/integration/diversity/wondrousness

E+

In turn, this C+ drives the universe towards what Birnbaum coins as Extraordinariation (shorthand: E+). Extraordinariation is a goal/horizon of sublime and utter super-Complexification – both in form and quality (see www.summametaphysica.com/extraordinariation/).

The three key components noted just-above, in turn combine into the SuperLaw of Potentialism:

The SuperLaw of Potentialism Theory

Q4P > C+ > E+

or

Quest for Potential > Complexification > Extraordinariation

Potentialism Theory: Historical Context

While Potentialism Theory is the first of its kind to enter the realms of physics and mathematics, some of its core ideas reverberate in classical philosophy. From the works of Pythagoras to those Plato and Aristotle, some of the underlying concepts of Potentialism are refined, but not thoroughly new. Let us explore some the classic philosophical works of antiquity that are represented in Potentialism.

Pythagoras and the primacy of mathematics

To Pythagoras, the universe was governed by mathematics. He observed not only the orderly motion of heavenly bodies but its echoes in music. One of the first to recognize the earth as round, Pythagoras proved insightful beyond his time. His work in music was a study of numerics in music, noting harmonics were based on the mathematics of such properties as string lengths.

While Pythagoras' understanding of the cosmos was primitive and, ultimately, incorrect in a lot of instances, he did understand that the universe was governed by mathematical principle. It cannot be overstated how groundbreaking this was at the time.

David Birnbaum himself has revisited this assumption, but with the tools of modern mathematics, science and metaphysics at his disposal. Indeed, he has gone far to prove the universal math of the cosmos in his theory of Potentialism. Birnbaum shows that the universe is governed, in its entirety, on the mathematical principle of Infinite Potential. Far beyond simple macro or micro physics, Birnbaum has given the 21st century the key to understanding the interrelationship between matter, energy, thought and even emotion – all governed by one overriding principle, Potential.

Plato and the Demiurge

Plato, by comparison, is the father of the concept of the "demiurge." Unlike the superstitions of other Greeks, Plato envisioned the creator of the universe, not as a human styled ruler of the cosmos, but as a "craftsman." To Plato, the creator was a worker and an artist who sculpted the universe in the form of a predetermined pathway. The demiurge did not invent – it instead imposed form on the formless along a pre-determined pathway.

Birnbaum and Potentialism:

The Demiurge – Plato's universal craftsman. This is most closely aligned with Birnbaum's Q4P (infinite Quest for Potential). It is the eternal spark that drives creation and Complexity.

The Form – This, to Plato, is the perfect form things in the universe strive to be. This concept is very similar to Extraordinariation – it is a hyper state of perfection – something which can be strived for but never perfectly attained.

Imitation of the model (Form) – Plato describes this as what exists in the universe, the tangible forms that seek to emulate the perfect form. Birnbaum describes this as current reality as it moves towards greater levels of perfection/Complexity.

The Receptacle – Plato describes the Receptacle as the place where everything in reality becomes. Birnbaum describes a similar concept of the Cosmic Womb. While Plato's receptacle only properly identified where matter, Birnbaum's Cosmic Womb describes the "space" in which everything becomes – matter, energy, thought and expression.

In many ways, Birnbaum picked up where Plato left off. Using some of the core concepts, devoid of Plato's mistakes, Birnbaum shows that, nevertheless, many of Plato's base concepts have modern day applications in cosmology to this date. Birnbaum is able to take what basic concepts Plato conceived and filter them for quality and validity through the lens of modern day science.

Aristotle and teleology

Another predecessor to a piece of Potentialism Theory is accredited to Aristotle – teleology.

"A teleology is any philosophical account that holds that final causes exist in nature, meaning that — analogous to purposes found in human actions — nature inherently tends toward definite ends."

Aristotle rejected the idea that everything in the world happens without purpose. Specifically, when viewing nature, Aristotle found it absurd that everything happens without a final cause in mind. To Aristotle, the natural world was capable of acting with extrinsic finality. That is to say, it could behave with an external end goal in mind – like when a person does something for a loved one with no gain of their own.

While this was highly contested during Aristotle's time, Birnbaum has picked up the banner for teleology. This might seem a daring maneuver, but as it turns out teleology has faced off well with critics in modern times. Central to Potentialism, Q4P is a pervasive teleological force. It defines how and why the universe progresses towards Complexity.

the Greeks?

How did the (great) Greeks totally miss Q4P∞

Philosophers were looking for an entity, not a force

Furthermore, the 'force' here is actually a 'quest'

And, in any event, philosophers were geared towards parsing the dimensions of classic God, as opposed-to totally **replacing** classic (dynamic and thoroughly conscious) God with a new paradigm '*something*'..... still it is 'curious'

A psychologist in the audience at one of my lectures opined that Q4P∞ did not want to be discovered until now - for whatever combination of reasons it might have - and *our psyches were consequently cloaked* hitherto (by Q4P∞) on that point

Others conjecture that a certain level of Evolutionary consciousness had to be reached before the theory could be conceptualized - and understood - and then accepted; that, the concept of a metaphysical quest (for an intangible - 'potential') driving the Cosmic Order would have been "a bridge too far" to reach any traction whatsoever hitherto

Conceptual Theorist

Remember, I view myself as a

Conceptual Theorist / Metaphysicist

and not as a

Scientist / Physicist

Simultaneously, however, my theory must dovetail with *good science.****

Good science, in turn, would not include the 'quack pseudo-science' of the Randomness gang,
nor with their assorted academic and media perversions. .

As noted, Potentialism Theory is proven inductively -
see Inductive1000.com

Another way of saying that is that -

>> No data point known to mankind conflicts with Potentialism Theory <<

See www.SummaCoverage.com

(see also Deductive1000.com)

our 'Smart Universe' driven by our hypothesized *natural force* (Q4P)

*** Of course, by the 2050, the science community may just cite the historic axiom -

>> **All science must comport to the governing Metaphysics** <<

21st CENTURY PUBLISHING
150+ AUTHORS/SCHOLARS

continue >

MORPHED COSMIC ORDER

Section L

MORPHED COSMIC ORDER

Birnbaumian Evolution

POTENTIALISM THEORY

Darwin's
Random Gene Mutation
is not the dynamic driving Evolution
*
rather, Potentialism's
tweaking of the genomes by Q4P$^\infty$
is the actual dynamic driving Evolution

"a unified metaphysics"

POTENTIALISM THEORY

- Louis Dupre'
Sterling Professor of Philosophy, YALE

"We hope to [eventually] explain
the entire universe in a simple formula
you can put on your T-shirt"

POTENTIALISM THEORY

- Leon Lederman, Texas, 1983
Nobel Prize in Physics

'ending the game' >

POTENTIALISM THEORY

- of Theory-of-No-Theory Randomness

---

unique / creative / original / paradigm-buster

POTENTIALISM THEORY

respectfully, standing the test of time
[1988 > present]

---

the T-Shirt Formula

POTENTIALISM THEORY

Q4P$^\infty$ > C+ > E+
[one-size-fits-all]

MORPHED COSMIC ORDER

"Bard College Conference"

AT BARD
APRIL 2012

POTENTIALISM THEORY

BARD COLLEGE
A PLACE TO THINK

THREE+ DAY
INTERNATIONAL ACADEMIC CONFERENCE

SCIENCE & RELIGION

with a focus on
Summa Metaphysica
by David Birnbaum

Monday through Thursday
April 16-19, 2012
Annandale-on-Hudson, NY

www.Conference1000.com

David Birnbaum's 'Quest for Potential' hypothesis

unifying science-spirituality-religion

International Academic Conference

Science and Religion:

A Role for Metaphysics?

Reflections flowing
from David Birnbaum's *Summa Metaphysica*

**"Works by David Birnbaum... suggest that Metaphysics
may emerge as a critical field once again."** *

- Dr. Bruce Chilton, co-Chairman
- Dr. Gary Hagberg, co-Chairman

AT BARD
APRIL 2012

- from Official Program Invitation & Introduction**
BARD College Conference, April 16-19, 2012

* [Meaning, after 300 year hiatus post-Spinoza]

** Conference1000.com

expanded

Science and Religion:

A Role for Metaphysics?

Reflections flowing from David Birnbaum's *Summa Metaphysica*

Discussion of the relationship between science and religion has typically proceeded on the basis of a scientific analysis of religion or a religious evaluation of science. Predictably, the cognitive lens of assessment has determined that the result will be either predominantly scientific or predominantly religious.

Since the nineteenth century the study of Metaphysics has usually been pursued within the history of philosophy. Advances in several disciplines, scientific and literary, as well as historical and philosophical, appeared to preclude understanding Metaphysics as an analytic discipline.

Yet as the twentieth century progressed, science offered the uncertainty principle, literature discovered hermeneutics that explained how one horizon or discourse may merge into another, history changed its key from the study of atomistic data to the unfolding of meaning, and philosophy challenged empirical constructions of reality. Works by David Birnbaum, chiefly his two volumes entitled Summa Metaphysica (1988 and 2005), suggest that Metaphysics may emerge as a critical field once again.

The presentations at the conference are open, and members of the community at Bard College are warmly invited. We are especially pleased to announce that David Birnbaum will be present during discussion.

Bruce Chilton
Bernard Iddings Bell Professor of Religion

Garry Hagberg
James H. Ottaway Jr. Professor of
Aesthetics and Philosophy

AT BARD
APRIL 2012

2012: "UNCONDITONAL LOVE"

THE CONFERENCE CHAIRMEN *FRONT & CENTER*

TO VIEW CO-CHAIRMAN BRUCE CHILTON BARD CONFERENCE OPENING
KEYNOTE ADDRESS
AND
CO-CHAIRMAN GARY HAGBERG CHAIRING MAIN CONFERENCE PANEL,

see www.SummaTapes.com
(scroll to 2012)

[important note on Conference Book]
www.ConferenceBook1000.com

not a dinner party

"A revolution is not a *dinner party*....A revolution is an *insurrection*"

—— Mao Tse-Tung

Bard Conference (2012) and other Potentialism Theory tapes

see SummaTapes.com

BARD CONFERENCE CHAIRMEN TAPES

Conference Opening: Summa, Gnosticism & Kabbalah / Panelist's Discussion

Dr. Bruce Chilton, Conference Chair, presiding / International Academic Conference
David Birnbaum's Summa Metaphysica / BARD College / April 16, 2012

-Part 1-

-Part 2-

Conference Finalé: Panel Discussion

Dr. Gary Hagberg, Conference co-Chair presiding / International Academic Conference David
Birnbaum's Summa Metaphysica / BARD College / Apr 18, 2012

-Part 1-

-Part 2-

-Part 3-

-Part 4-

see ConferenceTapes.com

August 21, 2016
↓ A.M. "Bard Grads / Millennials" Panel Summa Metaphysica
- with David Birnbaum

August 21, 2016
↓ P.M. "Bard Grads / Millennials" Panel Summa Metaphysica
- with David Birnbaum

David.Birnbaum.NY@gmail.com

Brit Peter Atkins

Celebrated British Chemist; Randomnist;
Poster Boy for Hard-Line Atheism

To his credit, (the stellar) Atkins was a full-scale Panelist at the Bard / Summa Conference.

A major component of the Conference were the lunch and dinner meals together - about 16 participants total.

I had read two* of Atkins' major works prior to the Conference in-prep; however, Atkins was aloof - and hard to draw-out. After frustration at meal #1, I assigned my 19 year-old son to sit directly opposite him (at all the meals) and try to engage, but they 'talked past each other'.

I do not believe Atkins ever 'got' what I was proposing. On the final full day of the Conference I chatted with him, and I offered to debate him - in USA or England at any time; but he did not seem to relish the thought.

Atkins is a Fellow at Oxford - which led us to absolve Oxford from the severe *abuse tsunami* which would emanate from England. The storm commenced ~90 days after the Conference - and was to span almost two years - across multiple fronts.

I believe only Atkins' quite-high stature in England saved him from vengeance-destruction by his British academic cohorts - for *de facto* giving his (powerful) imprimatur to the ('heretical') renegade Directional Universe Conference.

I have a separate exhibit in Chronology1000.com (printed in this volume first) - **Major Problems in (Establishment) Science** - (accurately) articulated by Atkins in his work *On Being* - but all 'resolved' by Summa;
the 'major problems' were the reason I started my quest in the first place;
thus, hard-line Atheist Atkins had a lot to be concerned about during - and after - the Conference. His high profile / stellar world was being upended - at its roots.

But again, on net balance, *kudos* to him for his formal participation.

* Galileo's Finger (2003)
  On Being (2011)

"the desire for a unified world picture is irrepressible"

Nagel

Argument by Thomas Nagel
NYU University Professor
in the Department of Philosophy and Law

in his very recent MIND & COSMOS
Oxford University Press (c) 2012

Professor Thomas Nagel argues passionately and articulately
(see chapters 1 and 2) that -

(a) we must search for an objectively palatable transcending view/schema
   of the cosmic order, and that

(b) the 'essential character' of such an understanding would be to explain
   the origins and existence of -
      - life
      - consciousness
      - reason
      - knowledge
      - altruism

without resort to theism - *from without*
but rather as a direct logical consequence of the overarching order
that governs the natural world - *from within*

Nagel argues that the origin and evolution of life and mind/consciousness
simply is not - and will not be - explainable by physics and chemistry alone.

"An expanded, but still unified, form of explanation will be needed, and I
suspect it will have to include teleological [goal-of-the-universe] elements".
(p. 33)

Nagel articulates (chapter 3) that 'the desire for a unified world picture is
irrepressible'.

New Paradigm Matrix respectfully offers
Summa Metaphysica's Quest for Potential° Theory.

David.Birnbaum.NY@gmail.com

Quest for Potential (Potential (Potential (Potential (Potential (

The Cosmic *Spinal Column* of Potential

$Q4P^∞$ Eternal

$Q4P^∞$ yields(advanced) Physics *et al.*

$Q4P^∞$ embracing/adhering-to all

$Q4P^∞$ ignites the universe

$Q4P^∞$ as catalyst for Life

$Q4P^∞$ as the spinal column of myriad Life

$Q4P^∞$ driving Evolution forward

$Q4P^∞$ as the central nervous system of Consciousness

$Q4P^∞$ gives Purpose

$Q4P^∞$ driving the universe forward

$Q4P^∞$ as teleology. The goal: Potential/ Extraordinariation

Birnbaum's Quest for Potential$^\infty$ hypothesis:

An Overarching Simultaneous Solution?

What is the value of an elegant/concise/original/grasp-able concept/dynamic - expressable in a simple formula: Q4P$^\infty$ -
which simultaneously seems to be a key missing 'building block" towards a solution of the salient major classic and contemporary macro-challenges in -

philosophy & metaphysics & physics & theology

including, amongst others:

theogony

cosmology / cosmogony

theodicy

purpose question

teleology

*

philosophy of science

Goldilocks Enigma

a unified scientific theory

*

Q4P$^\infty$

meaning, Quest for Potential (infinitely recursive

Q4P (Q4P (Q4P ...

meaning Quest for Potential within Potential within Potential........

What is the value of the Summa hypothesis if it has withstood 25+ years of international academic scrutiny - with no flaw or vulnerability found ?

Summa Metaphysica   www.Philosophy1000.com   NPM1000@yahoo.com

see also SimultaneousSolution.com

David Birnbaum / Summa Metaphysica / Potentialism Theory

Unifying Science, Religion & Philosophy

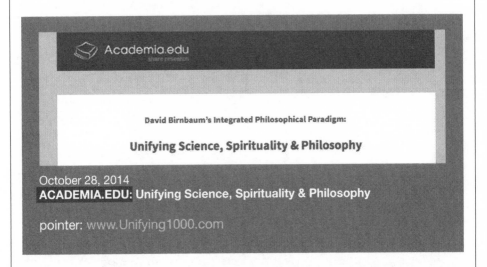

David Birnbaum's Integrated Philosophical Paradigm:

Unifying Science, Spirituality & Philosophy

October 28, 2014
ACADEMIA.EDU: Unifying Science, Spirituality & Philosophy

pointer: www.Unifying1000.com

Home About Us Print Editions Subscribe RSS Feeds Forum

EPOCH TIMES

February 6, 2015 | Languages ˅   35 Countries, 21 Languages, and Growing

HOME NEW YORK CHINA HK US WORLD OPINION BUSINESS TECH SCIENCE HEALTH FOOD & DINING ARTS ENTERTAINMENT LIFE TRAVEL SP

LIFE
Tikkun Olam & David Birnbaum's Summa Metaphysica

February 6, 2015
EPOCH TIMES: Tikkun Olam & David Birnbaum's Summa Metaphysica

https://www.summametaphysica.com/tikkun-olam/
OR
see Summa-Supplement.com   (100+ articles)

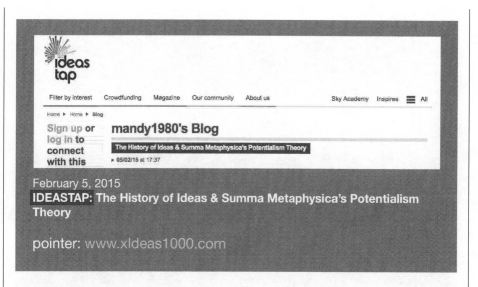

February 5, 2015
IDEASTAP: The History of Ideas & Summa Metaphysica's Potentialism Theory

pointer: www.xIdeas1000.com

February 4, 2015
FUTURE TECH: The Birnbaum Theorem

pointer: www.Theorem1000.com

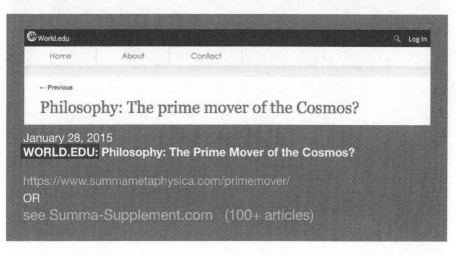

January 28, 2015
WORLD.EDU: Philosophy: The Prime Mover of the Cosmos?

https://www.summametaphysica.com/primemover/
OR
see Summa-Supplement.com   (100+ articles)

The Singularity of the Big Bang:
David Birnbaum's Summa Metaphysica

November 20, 2014
ACADEMIA.EDU: The Singularity of the Big Bang:
Juxtaposing Entrenched Orthodoxy Theory v. Potentialism Theory

https://www.summametaphysica.com/singularity/
OR
see Summa-Supplement.com (100+ articles)

Home   About   Stock Market News   Terms   RSS: Feed   Comments

Rocket News

The Core DNA of the Cosmic Order

November 20, 2014
ROCKET NEWS: The Core DNA of the Cosmic Order

pointer: www.DNA1000.com

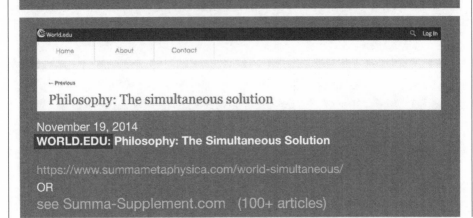

World.edu   Log In

Home   About   Contact

← Previous

Philosophy: The simultaneous solution

November 19, 2014
WORLD.EDU: Philosophy: The Simultaneous Solution

https://www.summametaphysica.com/world-simultaneous/
OR
see Summa-Supplement.com (100+ articles)

November 9, 2014
NEW ZEALAND TIMES: God Does Not Play Dice with the Universe

https://www.summametaphysica.com/dice-einstein/
OR
see Summa-Supplement.com   (100+ articles)

June 4, 2014
EPOCH TIMES: Birnbaum's Beethoven or Darwin's Beethoven

https://www.summametaphysica.com/beethoven/
OR
see Summa-Supplement.com   (100+ articles)

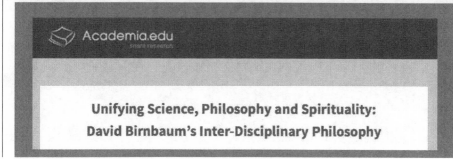

April 8, 2014
ACADEMIA.EDU: Unifying Theory: The Quest to Unify Science, Philosophy and Spirituality

https://www.summametaphysica.com/unifying-theory/
OR
see Summa-Supplement.com (100+ articles)

Future Technology
Virginia Polytechnic Institute and State
University in Blacksburg

February 25, 2013
7000 Years in the Making

Feb 25, 2014
FUTURE TECH: 7000 Years in the Making

https://www.summametaphysica.com/future-tech/
OR
see Summa-Supplement.com (100+ articles)

www.SummaMetaphysica.com
or
www.SmartUniverse1000.com

Why do you insist....

"Why do you insist that the universe is not a conscious intelligence, when it gives birth to conscious intelligence"

- Cicero, c. 44 BCE

*

Remember, Potentialism Theory does not go so far as to say that the universe is a '**conscious intelligence**'; rather, that the prime underlying dynamic (Q4P∞) is a **hyper-intelligence**.

Indeed, per the theory, humans (and the universe) are created, in part, to *vicariously* secure 'consciousness' for the the underlying dynamic Q4P∞.

PROVEN INDUCTIVELY

Harvard Kennedy School

What Ignited our Cosmos? (public group)

October 7, 2014

Deductive v. Inductive approach

Traditional academics have tackled the origins and nature of the universe through deductive reasoning. Looking back in time, they study the nature of the universe as it is and as far back as they can, and deductively try to reason out its secrets and origin. They've never succeeded. Looking back in time as the sole path to discerning the secrets of cosmic origins is problematic; the approach ultimately breaks down. It is true that scientists can look back a long way; with the powerful telescopes of today, they can look back very close to the time of the Big Bang, ferreting out many cosmic secrets. But there's a problem with attempting to deploy that approach alone in tracking back to "the beginning."

As you go back far enough, the very things which scientists measure begin to lose meaning. When approaching "the beginning" there are unavoidable issues. Indeed, the very word "beginning" loses meaning. In "the beginning" time did not exist. Indeed, matter as we know it did not exist either. Hence, the idea that science can look back all the way to and before the Big Bang through deductive reasoning is pretty much an exercise in futility.

Yeshiva and Harvard-educated David Birnbaum is a Manhattan-based private scholar who engages with these issues. His universe-theory has been featured globally. He employs both paths in-tandem. Since one cannot deduce the eternality of the cosmos simply (deductively) by working backwards in time, one must as well (inductively) start at "the beginning" and work forward.

MORPHED COSMIC ORDER

Birnbaum, in parallel to the ancient Greek metaphysicists, simultaneously starts with a proposed Eternal Origin and works forward towards Theoretical Physics. Birnbaum audaciously wants to seamlessly connect the two, and he apparently succeeds. "Outsider" to the formal academic establishment Birnbaum de facto simultaneously solves the inter-related series of classic (hitherto intractable) problems which has vexed the "insider" academic community.

Now, in order to build a theory inductively, it is important to have a defined set of assumptions which the starting premise (the transcendent dynamic to be discovered) must fulfill. Birnbaum defines these criteria as follows: (1) The system must be elegant. (2) Such a system would most probably be 'hidden in plain sight,' as it must be pervasive and universal. (3) Its core dynamic/concept must effectively be eternal. (4) The core dynamic must have a force-multiplier aspect and be able to project and impact infinitely forward.

In 1982 at age thirty-two Birnbaum finally vectored onto the concept/theme/dynamic he had been seeking. It would satisfy all of the above just-noted four criteria. The breakthrough would ultimately herald a possible Intellectual Revolution of the first magnitude – with profound implications.

Birnbaum's Theory of Potential would be the foundation of Summa Metaphysica – a treatise which would completely redefine current Universal Theory. Summa focuses on Birnbaum's signature concept of Potential. To Birnbaum, Potential has many faces: Quest for Potential∞, Infinite Potential, Cosmic Womb of Potential and related. All are different facets of the same universal dynamic.

Birnbaum proposes that Quest for Potential (iterated and nested to the infinite power) ignited and drives the cosmic order. Does this proposal satisfy Birnbaum's own four criteria?

(1) The proposal definitely satisfies the rule of elegance. The entry-point is simple: potential. But philosophically that simple statement has far reaching ramifications when examining the derivative conclusions this creates. If everything in the universe is pivoted on potential, we humans are potential in corporeal form.

(2) Its all-inclusiveness satisfies rule number two: It is indeed 'hidden in plain sight' by virtue of its own omnipresence and intangibility.

(3) Birnbaum daringly posits that Potential is eternal. Stated simply: We all exist; therefore, we all must have had the Potential to exist. Thus, the crucial "bullet proof" dimension of the theory: By definition, Potential is eternal. Its eternality is ultimately self-evident. Thus, its universal nature satisfies rule three as Potential is eternal – by definition.

(4) This Potentiality, when drawn to its logical conclusion, would encompass sub-creations (like humans) from these potentialities as well. Furthermore, what is currently in the universe carries the infinite potential for what can potentially be in the universe. Hence, Potential satisfies the fourth criteria as well.

Birnbaum took this simple, elegant theory and used it to tackle some of the most persistent questions in philosophy: Eternal Origins (his original question), Theogony (the existence and nature of the proposed divine), Theodicy (the problem of evil), Cosmology/Cosmogony (the origins and drive of the universe) and the Teleology Question (the purpose of respectively, both mankind and the universe).

The Manhattan author tackles all these issues in an exhaustive three-part treatise Summa Metaphysica I: Religious Man: God and Evil (Ktav1988); Summa Metaphysica II: Spiritual Man: God and Good (New Paradigm Matrix 2005); Summa Metaphysica III: Secular Man: The Transcendent Dynamic (New Paradigm Matrix 2014). See www.SummaMetaphysica.com.

While Birnbaum is a 'universalist,' avoiding judgment in the intense fundamentalist religious v. hard-line atheist argument, his work necessarily addresses these two sides. Unavoidably, Potential Theory provides (a) an eternal divine origin – infinite potential, (b) a scientific "design schema" (c) a scientific alternative to helter-skelter Randomness and (d) a functional theodicy (If God, why evil?) solution. Any one of the four components would be (fatally) radioactive to the entrenched hard-line Randomness-atheistic dogma. Summa shocks the atheistic 'entrenched dogma' in the academic community by serving-up all four solutions simultaneously – and via one term (potential).

First, Birnbaum has shown a trajectory from infinity past to the present and onward to infinity beyond of his signature concept of Infinite Potential. The universe journey is not random; it has a direction; one can even hypothesize this dynamic as the core of the Divine.

Second, Summa proposes that there not only is "design" to the universe, but that the designer is science itself. According to Birnbaum Infinite Potential harnessed the eternal equations of Physics-Math to ignite the cosmic order (see www.ParadigmChallenge.com).

Third, Summa shows that the alternative to Randomness-atheism is not (supernatural) Creationism, but rather (science-friendly) Potentialism. The entrenched orthodoxy scientific community assumes that to concede any "design" in the universe is to concede that (supernatural) God created it. Birnbaum demonstrated how their key debating premise was a fatally-flawed assumption and argument. The "designer" can be hypothesized to be Birnbaum's conceptually lean and fully scientific Infinite

Potential and not a supernatural Creationist Divinity.

While Birnbaum posits in Summa I that the spark of the divine/religious is inherent in Potential, and uniquely anchors religion metaphysically, he does not stake out a fundamentalist position as axiomatic; rather as a viable option. Birnbaum is not proposing "the supernatural" as the bedrock dynamic; he is proposing "the natural." His wide-spectrum theory, embracing religion and spirituality as options side-by-side with science, all in turn anchored by Infinite Potential, totally undermines the hard-line atheist arguments that absolutely the only alternative to atheism is Creationism.

Fourth, Summa shows that Potential can be used to address and resolve the pivotal theodicy issue (If God, why Evil?). The inescapable reality is that Summa I resolves the theodicy conundrum, hitherto the salient problem and Achilles' heel in religious philosophy (also for a long, long time).

This seemingly lethal quadruple-barreled hit on the entrenched Randomness-atheistic dogma has apparently fueled anger, if not panic, in segments of the atheist-controlled academic hierarchy. Believing that they had securely, if not permanently, entrenched their dogma into Academe via squelching all debate, the academic power hierarchy was incensed that Birnbaum had done an end-run around their intellectual blockade via the 4-day international academic Bard Conference which exclusively featured his work. All subsequent attempts by the 'entrenched dogma' group to suppress Birnbaum's theory and suppress his theory have hitherto backfired.

The Transcendent Force

Birnbaum lays out the dramatic 1:1 parallel between his theory (1988, 2005) and the 2006 book of Quantum Physicist Seth Lloyd of MIT. Birnbaum cites Lloyd "The universe computes its own behavior…its own dynamic evolution." Birnbaum's Theory of Potential actually elegantly wraps-around Lloyd's theory and fills-in key gaps. Birnbaum's theory provides (a) a catalyst, (b) a driver, and (c) a (more sophisticated) goal for Lloyd's proposed universal quantum mechanism.

Birnbaum's Infinite Potential itself is the prime mover, the catalyst for life and the alpha and omega. Indeed, it is Infinite Potential which defines the universe and lies at the fount of science, philosophy and spirituality. All three seemingly disparate fields intersect with Infinite Potential at their core; Infinite Potential is the cosmic nexus point.

Accolades from the academic/scientific community

Universally acclaimed metaphysics expert Louis Dupré, Professor of Religious Studies, Yale University (1989) calls Summa I "an original and in this reader's opinion, a very promising point of view…the author gathers a philosophically coherent and, in the end, highly modern insight…a unified metaphysics…"

Dr. Andrei Alyokhin, Associate Professor School of Biology and Ecology University of Maine wrote in November 2012 "Summa represents a bold attempt to formulate a unifying concept of the Universe…. Therefore, it is reasonable to propose the Quest for Potential∞ as a working hypothesis for explaining the impetus behind the cosmic dynamic."

Birnbaum's Potentialism Theory has garnered solid backing from eclectic members of Academe globally (see www.PotentialismTheory.com). In the twenty-six years since it was introduced in 1988, no flaw has been discerned in the metaphysically and scientifically unifying thesis.

Other works

Birnbaum, in addition to Potential Theory, has written a number of other important works including a 7-volume series, which tracks the 4,000 year history of the Jews through important civilizations, titled Jews, Church and Civilization. He is currently editor-in-chief of a potentially landmark 10-volume series on Jewish spirituality Mesorah Matrix scheduled to be released in segments between 2014 and 2019. This series brings together the essay contributions of over 150 Jewish thought leaders from around the world. The series allows Birnbaum, the universalist, to wear a different hat as editor of a series focused on spirituality. But, as he points out, to avoid inserting editorial bias into his metaphysics, he is not an essay contributor to the spirituality series, and his role is strictly as the series catalyst and editor-in-chief.

Context

A Course Text at over a dozen colleges (see www.SummaCourseText.com), Summa Metaphysica has been the focus of over seventy feature articles in 2013-2014 alone. See www.SummaCoverage.com.

Summa Metaphysica – and its Theory of Potential – was the focus of a 3+ day international academic conference at Bard College (Upstate, NY) April 2012; the conference, which launched Summa globally, created a global **academic firestorm**.

Recent hi-level academic works dovetailing with Birnbaum's Theory of Potential include the following:

Programming the Universe (Knopf, 2006) by Professor of Quantum Mechanics Seth Lloyd of MIT; Mind & Cosmos (Oxford Press, 2012) by Professor of Philosophy & Law Thomas Nagel of NYU; Our Mathematical Universe (Knopf, 2014) by Professor of Physics Max Tegmark of MIT.

MORPHED COSMIC ORDER

Section M

MORPHED COSMIC ORDER

"Spinoza and Birnbaum
are paradigm-breaking philosophers
who have shaped the study of philosophy"

POTENTIALISM THEORY

CNN iReport 4/9/14

the holy grail of metaphysics

POTENTIALISM THEORY

simple, but *not-so-simple*

THE BIRNBAUM TELEOLOGY
[ncluding on both macro and micro levels]

POTENTIALISM THEORY

$Q4P^\infty > C+ > E+$

Potentialism Theory's Teleology
[$Q4P^\infty > C+ > E+$]

POTENTIALISM THEORY

is a *'stake in the heart'*
of Theory-of-No-Theory Randomness

our extra-smart universe

POTENTIALISM THEORY

designed by an ever-iterating and extra-smart
universal & pinnacle natural
Designer-Force [$Q4P^\infty$]

MORPHED COSMIC ORDER

In summary, to be considered:

Summa presents an Overarching Metaphysics:
a unifying concept of the universe.

Summa Theory pegs-off of one single unique concept/dynamic -
Quest for Potential$^\infty$
to craft a unified/elegant/original/powerful/consistent metaphysics.

This concept is by definition Eternal. That is *self-evident* in this case.

Q4P$^\infty$ captures the entire cosmic dynamic in one
simple-yet-sophisticated
concise/elegant/efficient/comprehensible formula.

Meaning, the concept - Q4P$^\infty$ - is simultaneously the formula.

No flaw - or weakness - has been discerned in the Theory.
[The core theory was presented/published in November 1988 via Summa I
(KTAV Publishing). The core theory has not morphed.]

Summa Theory 'handles' the key Metaphysics questions,
and potentially elegantly fills-in key gaps in science.

Respectfully, Summa Theory has no competition.
Meaning, there is no Option #B on-the-table *from any quarter.*

Q4P$^\infty$ is 'infinite', 'nested', and indeed, uniquely 'infinitely nested'.

Summa fights neither Religion nor Science.
Indeed, Summa Theory wraps-around all (repeat: all) scientific fact.

Summa Theory actually 'reasonably' handles
            origin/nurturing/development of - the universe, life,
consciousness

Summa works *across-the-board*: Its cosmology dovetails elegantly with its
theogony, theodicy, purpose-question and teleology.

The odds are respectable that Summa Theory is conceptually
on-the-mark.   *

our 'Smart Universe' driven by our hypothesized *natural force* (Q4P)

The "Cosmic Womb of Potential"
An encapsulation of the Summa metaphysics

In the void of voids,
there was only Potential/Possibility

- an eternal dynamic

Morphing-into and coursing-through the metaphysical
Cosmic Womb of Potential

Its goals...

short-term:	Traction
Intermediate:	A panoply of Potential
ultimate:	Extraordinariation

The equations of mathematics and physics would come early-on

In turn, the broader array of equations would radiate outwards.

In turn, seeking/yearning-for -
Expression, Reality, Feeling, Emotion
Life Hope Dreams Consciousness Love Drama *et al.*

The "0"- Point Portal.

But, first a universe was needed...

And only '0' existed as a possible bridge to reality... But, that would suffice.

The equations – driven by Infinite Divine Potential -
would conspire/collaborate
to split '0'
- and unleash its possibly infinite Potential

So, a few billion years before Einstein *et al.* would split the atom
and unleash the atom bomb...

the equations would collaborate to split '0'
- the potential Cosmic PORTAL
Metaphysical > Physical

and unleash the universe...

The frequencies and the dials were very exquisitely calibrated
    - to the now-iconic very-finely-tuned *"Goldilocks Constants"*

(for our, indded, *Fine-Tuned Universe*)

The Countdown... *The Launch*

The Genesis Point

    aka The (very) Big Bang.

Splitting '0' into
    Positives and Negatives
    Female and Male
    Good and Evil
    Positive & Negative energy
    Regular & Dark matter

Potential would reign supreme.

To the spiritual, this Potential is the Metaphysical God of Potential:
    Eheyeh Asher Eheyeh:
    I Will Be That Which I Will Be (Book of Exodus 3:14)
    The Infinite Divine. *Shadai.* The Source. Holy Quest for Potential
    The kabbalistic *En Sof* ('The No-End')

See also *Anima mundi* - the 'world soul' - in Plato (Timaeus 29/30) *et al.*

Secular or Holy
    the grand cosmic journey / exploration / odyssey
        advances-onward to this day

With Freedom - integral to Potential - being axiomatically inviolate.
(Leaving *evil* un-checked.)
And Potential leading and integrating the cosmic advance

Daring
Optimizing
Advancing
Iterating
Harmonizing
Over-arching

Impacting all / All-embracing.

MORPHED COSMIC ORDER

Q4P Evolution: With Q4P ongoing choreographing - via quantum messaging - the tweaking of all genomes on a species level - is Q4P/Quantum directing evolution towards C+ while factoring-in the ultimate E+ trajectory.
[So, the Extended Evolutionary Synthesis will need to be overhauled.]

Quest for Potential$^\infty$ (Q4P$^\infty$)

Quest for Potential (Potential (Potential *ad infinitum*

Invisible, yet simultaneously in full-view

Hiding in plain sight / Beneath-the-radar

Smooth Operator

And we are all integral-to this mysterious Quest For Potential

Itself an integrated Infinitely nested Unity – encompassing all

…. *On a journey towards* ***Extraordinariation***

Advancing-through the sundry storms….

Life. Death	Dreams. Defeat	Re-birth. Destruction
Birth. Genocide	Respect. Defamation	Venerated. Terrorized
Glory. Humiliation	Loyalty. Betrayal	Breakthrough. Heartbreak
Mercy. Sadism	Gentleness. Abuse	Unconquered. Defiled
Pinnacle. Tears	Hope. Pain	Triumph. Despair

Quest for Potential$^\infty$ - on an eternal cosmic explorer expedition

probing and searching for (elusive) ultimate -

meaning….destiny…fulfillment….consciousness….harmony… beauty… grandeur….elegance….artistry… love…. spirituality... perfection…. humanitarianism….altruism

…the elusive ***Extraordinariation***

- a goal to be approached – like Infinity – even inexorably and indefatigably - but alas, destined to never quite be fully realized……..

ONWARD.

- Birnbaum

David.Birnbaum.NY@gmail.com

now, back to the 'beginning of the beginning'

Primordial Cosmic Realms*
working hypothesis

1) Potential/Possibility is eternal**

[But what is the catalyst morphing
(seemingly passive) Potential into (pro-active) Quest for Potential (Q4P)?]

2) Primordial (potential/possibility-oriented) **Quantum Mechanics (QM)*** and**
(eternal) **Potential** *supercharge* each other

   a) **Potential → Quest for Potential~ (Q4P)**
     [This 'quest' will have both *intentionality and ~instinct intelligence*]

   b) Primodial QM → Primodial+ QM

3) In due course, Q4P will deploy/harness both (pre-Big Bang primordial)
Quantum Mechanics (QM) and (pre-Big Bang primordial) Classic Physics
- to split 'ZERO' - and ignite our universe via the Big Bang.... *the Genesis Point.*

***

Creation Ex Nihilo+

So, it would seem that
   Creation Ex Nihilo
  (Creation from Nothing)
falls, as well, to Summa/Potentialism Theory

So we, indeed, would seem to have a viable metaphysical/scientific ('fusion' again)
working hypothesis for one of the iconic Holy Grails of metaphysics//philosophy/
cosmology

I might prefer to call the finesse -

.....*Creation Ex Nihilo+*

because

   Potential is more than Nothing

Basically, two potential-related 'somethings' *supercharge* each other -

Summa's metaphysical Eternal Potential was 'impacted' by the primordial incarnation (specifically, the potential-possibility aspect thereof, of) Planck/Einstein's Quantum Mechanics (QM) - to yield Summa's proposed Prime Mover (*primum movens*) Q4P

And this Prime Mover can be viewed as either secular or spiritual or Divine (or some variation thereof), depending on one's predilection.

*

Be clear that I did not (have the nerve to) mess around with integrating QM whatsoever into Summa/Potentialism Theory until I read Lloyd's ("Programing") book in 2006 - and observed the extraordinary 1:1 parallel to Summa I (1988) and Summa II (2005); however, like a stem cell, QM would seem to have many vibrant 'faces'... and thus, the QM plot thickened... *and here we are*

As you are aware, I integrate the Wheeler/Lloyd QM It/Bit build-out into my Summa/ Potentialism theory Evolution build-out several years later - in 2014 in Summa III; however, the above Primordial Cosmic Realms QM build-out is new****.

Be alert that, contrary to point (2) above, there are those who assert that QM does not exist (in any form) pre-Big Bang; respectfully, they are wrong*****; however, even if they are right, point (2) above will then simply need to be tweaked as follows .*The potential/possibility of (potential-possibility-oriented) QM jump-started Q4P from Eternal Potential.* ******

---

* before our universe was even created

** As noted, BY DEFINITION....Self-Evident

*** In our deployment of QM in primordial realms we are focusing on the classic 'possibility' aspect of QM; in our deployment of QM via a' vis Evolution we are focusing on the Wheeler/Lloyd 'bit-build-out aspect of QM.

**** I had 'radar lock' at post-Yom Kippur Break-Fast Sept 30, 2017 while harassing the (philosophically sharp)
NYU Medical School student next to me - after struggling with the issue for several decades.
As we were going down the NYU Kimmel Building elevator after the buffet, I asked him what he liked best
about the theory. His response: "It would appear to be a viable and quite all-encompassing theory; and in science the more all-encompassing viable theory prevails."

***** QM needs to be operational pre-Big Bang, because QM is (quite-specifically) needed to arrange the precise settings for the Big Bang; QM has the *tool-kit* to do same - and 100th generation IBM's Watson (c. 3000 CE) was not in the picture yet....

****** As is apparent, this (fallback) version would be weaker than my preferred version (above).

TITLE PAGE

A Formal Inductive Proof of

David Birnbaum's

Cosmological Theory of Potentialism

as presented in Birnbaum's
3-volume
Summa Metaphysica

[see www.SummaMetaphysica.com]

*

The 45 page proof - outline below - is crafted and presented

by

Mark Davis

and approved by D. Birnbaum

April 7, 2016

[note: we are only showing the first 1 ½ pages]

Forward

"... for we perceive that this miraculous development is not the result of our own efforts: an eternal Perfection is molding us into its own image."

—— *Sri Aurobindo*

As a chemist, mathematician, philosopher and person of faith, I have long been accustomed to wearing an ever changing assortment of hats. "Hard science" is the tool for everyday observation. As such, I have always followed the clean logic and well-rigored science of my peers when trying to understand the universe and how it could run with such wondrous, clock-work precision.

Yet there was always something lacking. Like putting a puzzle together only to find the picture would not make sense – something was missing. It never occurred to me that looking at the *what* of the universe would never truly lead me to the *why* of it. I could show how a star formed, but I could never actually answer *why* it formed. Why life existed. Why, even, the universe was here.

My faith was of little solace. I had wonderful parables on how to live a just and meaningful life, but as a tool of science and understanding it was meaningless. There was no reconciling Genesis with the observable universe. Genesis could only be considered seriously as yet another parable, a story devoid of real scientific information.

Likewise, philosophy gave me no insight. It was a wonderful tool for trying to discern the nature of consciousness and morality, but it offered little in the way of understanding the physical universe save for the outdated and incorrect geocentric Aristotelian and Platonic models.

Then I came across the work of **Manhattan cosmologist David Birnbaum.** His groundbreaking work on Potentialism Theory changed the very approach I had on cosmology. Potentialism provides a framework for understanding the universe by analyzing it through the lens of science, philosophy and even faith and spirituality. Where I was seeking the "best tool", it had never occurred to me I needed them all at once to see the "picture in the puzzle".

In this work, I intend to provide a layman's guide to the Theory of Potentialism in hopes to make the theory as accessible as possible for the broadest audience possible. Further, I seek to provide an inductive proof that will support the strength of this simple, yet powerful, theory.

I. Introduction

"The menu is not the meal."

- Alan W. Watts

In 1988, cosmologist David Birnbaum published the first of his three part **Summa Metaphysica** series. Within its pages contained the foundations of a new cosmological model which sharply diverged from commonly held scientific theories. Birnbaum would challenge directly the very preconceptions that bound then modern cosmology together.

To begin, Birnbaum would toss away several assumptions of modern physics. The most important of these would be the supremacy of quantifiable evidence. Physics and, more broadly, modern science is based on observation. More precisely, it is based on what can be measured and quantified - we test for elements with spectroscopy, we study movement with redshift, we weigh, we measure, we time, we calculate and we record. These are the tools of physics to understand the universe around us and they are excellent at performing their function.

see *inductive1000.com* for 40+ pg balance

David.Birnbaum.NY@gmail.com

RESOURCES

KEY RESOURCES FOR

Summa Metaphysica

[Potentialism Theory]

3-volume treatise*: Summa Metaphysica
see flip-books on
www.SummaMetaphysica.com

3 spinoffs*
www.SpinOffs1000.com

Main Summa Site
www.SummaMetaphysica.com

(sister) Summa Site
www.PotentialismTheory.com
includes BLOGS + Translations

'mother ship' Platform
www.NewParadigmMatrix.com

INTL Bard Conference
www.Conference1000.com

150+ articles, reviews on Summa
www.SummaCoverage.com

15+ colleges / Course Text
www.SummaCourseText.com

8-volume Potentialism Theory via Graphic Narrative
www.TheoryGraphics1000.com

YouTube - Summa / Potentialism
www.SummaTapes.com

Formal Inductive Proof
www.Inductive1000.com
(approximately 45-page)

Paradigm Challenge Scroll-Down
www.PotentialismTheory.com/ParadigmChallenge/

note that Summa / Potentialism Theory proposes a 'directional universe', No flaw has been discerned in the theory since it was first formally proposed in Summa I (God and Evil) in 1988.

A 'directional universe' frontally challenges/undermines the entrenched Atheistic/ Randomness establishment theory championed by players based in England. The virulent push-back from that quarter has not been intellectual, but *rather, ad hominem*.

* all Birnbaum works are available in 3 modalities:
HardCopy via Amazon; flip-bok (gratis- pro bono) on website; electronic

www.SummaMetaphysica.com
or
www.SmartUniverse1000.com

to order direct via Amazon click **SummaAmazon**

Running the Gauntlet ...

The author of a new theory is typically compelled to
'run a gauntlet of toxicity' before the new theory even gets a *fair hearing*

A sequenced list of toxic gambits deployed by entrenched orthodoxy academic establishments v. dynamic new paradigm theories follows:

First, the theory is **politically boxed-out**

Second, the theoretician/author is **dissed and/or defamed** - to undermine the theory

Third, the theory is **cavalierly dismissed**

Fourth, **fake flaws** in the theory are manufactured/asserted by the (now increasingly-desperate) Establishment

Fifth, the theory is **aggressively politically opposed** by the (now panicking) Establishment

Sixth, the (original) theory is challenged as being **not so original** in any event - by the (*now up against the wall*) Establishment

Seventh, in league with the Establishment, wannabe players attempt to **co-opt original authorship**

- extrapolation of saw/maxim
by Arthur Schopenhauer,
German philosopher
(1788-1860)

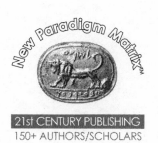

21st CENTURY PUBLISHING
150+ AUTHORS/SCHOLARS

continue >

MORPHED COSMIC ORDER

Section N

MORPHED COSMIC ORDER

THE UNIVERSE
IS CONTINUOUSLY, ONGOING >

POTENTIALISM THEORY

ITERATING & OPTIMIZING

---

a universal metaphysics via 4 lenses

POTENTIALISM THEORY

Religious Man (1988); Spiritual Man (2005);
Secular Man (2014); Quantum Man (2020)

WE ARE ALL STARDUST,

POTENTIALISM THEORY

BUT, WE ARE ALL ALSO ALL **POTENTIAL**

Q4P$^{\infty}$

POTENTIALISM THEORY

dependent on humankind for
consciousness & emotion

---

our purpose-driven universe

POTENTIALISM THEORY

MAXIMIZING/OPTIMIZING
OUR HUMAN POTENTIAL

MORPHED COSMIC ORDER

in summation

TWO OPTIONS

The two current salient
overarching paradigm options are:

RANDOMNESS theory
• Entrenched
• old paradigm
• aimless
• heir to alchemy
• a *Theory of No Theory*
• anti-scientific
• parochial / hard-line Atheistic / Fundamentalist
• no core text / no website
• hierarchy: secret / ~London / legally at-risk

or

POTENTIALISM theory
• Challenger
• new paradigm
• directional
• heir to Aristotelian 'directionalism'
• a well-vetted theory
• bullet-proof
• universalistic
• Summa Metaphysica 3-volume treatise*
• hierarchy: D. Birnbaum / Manhattan

*online *in toto*

our 'Smart Universe' driven by our hypothesized *natural force* (Q4P)

Comparison: God of Israel | Q4P

	God of Israel	Q4P$^\infty$
max consciousness	Y	N
transmutates	N	Y
morphs	N	Y
eternal	Y	~Y
legislates	Y	N
judgmental	Y	N
punishes	Y	N
potentially vengeful	Y	N
has emotion	Y	N
seeks emotion vicariously	N	Y
seeks greatest good for the greatest number	Y	Y
averse to evil	Y	Y
able to eliminate evil	N	N
IS everything	N	Y
directional universe	Y	Y
ostensibly creates a ~finished universe	Y	N
explicators allow for - or mandate - evolution	Y	Y
self-perceives itself as Divine	Y	N
seeks spirituality	N	M
seeks after God	N	M
origin explained	N	~Y
theogony issue remains?	Y	N
hyper-intelligent design?	Y	Y
centerpiece of a religion?	Y	N

M = Maybe

The Sanctity of Human Life

Per Potentialism Theory, the core of Life is $Q4P^\infty$

and $Q4P^\infty$ is more like an infinite metaphysical river.

Thus, murder, for instance,

would, as well, be an attack on the core of the Cosmic Order

- aside from the crime of the murder of the individual victim.

And, the human, after all, is the apex production (*to date*)

of Infinite Quest for Potential.

Transform1000.com

What comes next?

Our premise is that, aside from the broader goal
of Complexification enroute to Extraordinariation,
$Q4P^\infty$ seeks to (vicariously) play out dimensions of
Consciousness and Love.

So, following that thrust, no reason to doubt that $Q4P^\infty$
will seek to follow-up ongoing on those two thrusts.
And, one suspects that ever-expanding Consciousness
has priority between the two thrusts.

So, what does ever-expanding Consciousness imply?
I have not truly focused on that question, but I believe
that it is a very key question to be addressed by all.

Multiverse?

Are there infinite universes -
per many Darwinian apologists ?

several points -

#1 Any universe *requires Potential* at its core.

#2 Even with core Potential, the odds of *traction* are remote.

#3 Even if possible traction, the Cosmos *may not wish* to
invest/divert/deploy energy
in even one other universe (overlapping in time with our universe).

#4 "Infinite universes theory" *aka* 'multi-verse theory' is a dubious proposition,
albeit hypothetically possible; basically, the theory appears to be propped-up
to provide 'life support' to on-its-death-bed quack theory 'Randomness Theory' -
primarily after the book Just Six Numbers (by Royal Astronomer Martin Rees, 1999)
dealt a body-blow to the vacuous (Randomness) theory.

Major1000.com

What is the Lifespan of Q4P Universe?

Q4P has eternal origins
[see the *En Sof* primordial God of (kabbalist) Luria (b. 1534)]
[brought up in Summa 1 (1988)]

Q4P endeavors to be eternal going forward

Then, try to integrate the following to understand Q4P:

The universe is an evolvement of Q4P

We are all integral to Q4P/Universe

One can (optionally) posit that Q4P is the God Force

See (quick) Universe1000.com
(lead-in to RewindSumma.com)

See Chronology1000.com
(displayed, as well, in RewindSumma.com)

Note the (panentheistic) God of the BESHT
(the BESHT = the Baal Shem Tov, [b. 1698]
the spiritual founder of Hasidic Judaism)
[brought up in Summa 2 (2005)]

Seth Lloyd's Programming the Universe (2006)
[which builds upon John Wheeler's *It from Bit*]

possibly with Divine spark / drive

Remember the ALIEN sci fi series
(introduced 1979)
wherein the alien entity
learns, integrates, iterates,
and gets stronger daily

In our case, Q4P, a more benign entity, does same

i.e. We have a unique variation of Process Theology

An all-encompassing *suis generis*
self-iterating
AI
or
UI (Universe Intelligence)
(with Divine Spark/Drive in-the-mix?)
[of which WE are each components]
monitoring/tweaking/running/driving/iterating/morphing
the universe
- to optimize, among other objectives, *perpetual advance.*

Our universe - a potentially perpetual motion force/entity -
endeavors/iterates/morphs/maneuvers
to play-out
its *perpetual motion* potential

Thus, the potential - but far from guaranteed - lifespan of our
Q4P universe
is infnite

However, Q4P in its pure form is eternal, regardless

NOTE ON LIFESPAN

The Universe (aka Q4P) is expanding ongoing;
currently this expansion rate is accelerating.

Q4P must vigilantly advance forward
with sufficient (Lambda) velocity/force to
prevail against entropy.

Q4P must contend with gravity, as well,
which simultaneously
enhances, maintains, and threatens the universe.

LIKE

Why does this metaphysics trump all other metaphysics?

1) It is pegged to an *eternal* dynamic (Potential)

2) It is pegged to a proposed (hitherto undiscerned) *natural force* (Q4P) -
   as opposed-to a *supernatural force*
   or
   to a fatally flawed theory (Darwinism)

3) The theory is *all-embracing*

4) The theory has been (successfully) vetted ongoing since Summa I in 1988

5) The core theme - the Common Denominator of $Q4P^\infty$ -
   threads its way steadily and inexorably
   from Eternal Origins through the Big Bang
   through the current day - and onward

6) The theory allows optional space for a potential Divine 'instigator' at the *get-go*

7) The theory covers the key issues of classic and modern metaphysics:
   Eternal Origins; pre-Big Bang realms; the instigation of the Big Bang;
   the origin of our super-complex universe;
   the eerily fine-tuned myriad Constants;
   the origin and 'journey' of the 117+ Elements (to date);
   the origin of life; the ascent of evolution;
   the Cambrian Explosion;
   the expansion of consciousness

8) The theory frontally deals with 'purpose' (across the board), e.g. -
   # the purpose of Man (to strive for his Potential)
   # the purpose of the universe (to strive for Extrordinariation)

9) The theory provides a fresh - and credible - *theory of Evolution*

10) The theory helps to clarify Dark Energy and Dark Matter -
    and the associated *universal constant* (lambda)

11) The theory furnishes a SuperLaw to the universe:
     $Q4P^\infty \rightarrow C+ \rightarrow E+$
     - a formula which as been inductively 'proven'

12) The theory is organized, disciplined and charted

13) The theory is creative and original

14) The theory has proven-to-be 'bulletproof'

15) The theory thematically threads consistently through *pre* and *post* Big Bang

16) After 5,000+ years of civilization,
    there is no *bona fide* credible challenging theory.
    to Potentialism

17) The theory is highly ambitious, but does not overreach

18) One can *make the case* that this is a serious contender for a
    conceptual *Theory of Everything*

Cosmic Ironies

some counter-Intuitive ironies re: Q4P

$Q4P^\infty$ is the source of life in our universe,
   but is not itself *fully alive*

$Q4P^\infty$ crafted our universe,
   but *seeks after* God - its creator* - vicariously - via ourselves

$Q4P^\infty$ is practically all-knowing,
   but *seeks after* human-like consciousness via ourselves

* $Q4P^\infty$ quests for full understanding of its 'creator', and assumes -
   rightfully or wrongfully - that it has a classic creator.

**'Contemporary Jewish philosopher David Birnbaum'
quoted in psychoanalysis textbook 'Centers of Power':**

CENTERS OF POWER

THE CONVERGENCE OF PSYCHOANALYSIS AND KABBALAH

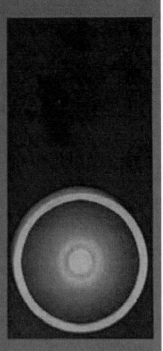

**JOSEPH H. BERKE AND
STANLEY SCHNEIDER**

The contemporary Jewish philosopher David Birnbaum adds to this picture by describing God and godliness in terms of the absolute potential to be what one can be, and to know what one can know. He notes that in the Torah, in the Book of Exodus, the name of God that was first proclaimed to Israel, *Eheyeh Asher Eheyeh,* means "I-Will-Be-That-Which-I-Will-Be."[11] From this he deduces that the name of God is essentially a statement that "the holiest state of the holy is God of Potential."[12] Birnbaum adds:

> God is the actualization of potential in its conscious holy form . . . holy potential within potential within potential *ad infinitum.* For the infinite God of Israel is a God of willed potential . . . [that] transcends time, space and the cosmos . . . rippling infinitely forward. . . .[13]

Birnbaum contrasts the 'Tree of Life' as in the Garden of Eden with the 'Tree of Knowledge.' While the 'Tree of Life' is associated with bliss and eternal life, he calls it a "gilded cage existence," a state of stasis with limited potential for growth or personal development, because life is predetermined. On the other hand he relates the 'Tree of Knowledge' to a life of challenge, freedom, responsibility, the pursuit of knowledge and infinite growth potential. Mankind comes into its own once it has tasted the fruit of the 'Tree of Knowledge.' Yes, this comes with pain, mortality and 'unleashed natural evil.' But it also releases joy, dignity and, especially, free will.[14]

Remaining attached, the 'Tree of Life' is akin to pre-birth, residing in the womb of God. But tasting the 'Tree of Knowledge' is akin to birth, with all the possibilities and difficulties that this entails. Far from committing a sin, by eating the apple of knowledge, Eve chose to choose life, the actualization of her potential as a woman and partner to Adam. Likewise Adam chose to be born with the potential for reaching for the infinite.[15] Birnbaum asserts, and many Kabbalists would agree, that this freedom to choose to reach for the infinite is the highest good and the ultimate purpose of 'man's' sojourn on earth.[16]

Spinoza1000.com

April 9, 2014

Spinoza v. Birnbaum

BREAKING NEWS   **Russia gives ultimatum to Ukrainian forces in Crimea: Clear out wi 11 hours or face 'military storm,' Russian state media report.**

SIGN U

CNN iReport   🔲 Main   🔍 Explore   ✓ Assignments   👤 Profile

Collision in Time

By Samna | Posted April 9, 2014

Let us juxtapose iconic philosopher Spinoza (1632-1677 CE) with cutting-edge contemporary conceptual theorist David Birnbaum (1950-present). You know them as two noteworthy metaphysics specialists, Baruch Spinoza of Amsterdam and the contemporary David Birnbaum of New York: Strong-willed intellectual revolutionary iconoclasts who challenged the entrenched status quo.

Both of these intellectually disciplined, but daring, thinkers sprang from within the Orthodox Jewish tradition; both pledged their allegiance to universalism; both gave full due to the authenticity of religion; both published groundbreaking philosophical treatises; and both experienced virulent personal attacks from assorted cliques of zealot defenders of the 'entrenched orthodoxy.'

A look at these two philosophical 'Jedi masters' demonstrates just how far the study of philosophy has come over the last three centuries. Spinoza and Birnbaum – each conceptually nimble, each respectively armed with a major treatise, separated by 350 years chronologically. They each launch major fields in the philosophical arena: Spinoza's Determinism, Birnbaum's Potentialism.

Their theories are each groundbreaking and unique, but there are also some extraordinary similarities. Across the centuries, their treatises 'speak to each other,' as if the treatises themselves are having a formal debate. Of course Birnbaum speaks last and is aware that Spinoza cannot rebut. As a consequence, Birnbaum is quite deferential to Spinoza.

Spinoza, the father of Determinism, set the groundwork for future Renaissance philosophers. He wrote his masterpiece "Ethics" in a powerful voice that provoked new ways of thinking. Spinoza believed that God was somewhat identical to Nature and the natural order. This God is an unknowable, impersonal entity who created everything as perfection, even evil. Spinoza states that evil is not deviance from perfection, but a part of it.

Spinoza's writings are not anti-religious, but his brazen voice and imperious attitude quickly caught the attention of the local rabbinic council, which excommunicated him for 'his attitude' when he was 23. He was even threatened with a knife outside a synagogue. It is just as well then, that Spinoza ended his formal education at age 17, providing himself some physical distance from the establishments he quarreled with. Despite his self-alienation from formal schooling, 'outsider' Spinoza has had a profound impact on the global intellectual world for the centuries subsequent.

A couple hundred years after Spinoza, 'outsider' David Birnbaum founded and championed Potentialism, which radically branches away from Spinoza's Determinism. Since 1988 Birnbaum has sequentially published a 3-volume treatise Summa Metaphysica (1988, 2005, 2014), which has come to be used as a course text at over a dozen universities. This breathtaking journey into Potentialism has tantalized many globally, but radically threatened a small segment. In any event, the theory is in position to shake the world. Potentialism is in that rare category of – simple, yet profound. Over a dozen journals have featured Birnbaum's Summa Metaphysica and its Theory of Potential. For theory core, see www.summametaphysica.com/theory-core/.

Birnbaum proposes that his signature theme of Infinite Potential (Quest for Potential infinitely nested) gifts humans complete freedom and that interference is not possible in a cosmic order underpinned by Potentialism. According to Potentialism the universe of necessity has in it both good and evil, a duality which must always exist; good and evil must inevitably spar. If there were no possibility for evil in the universe, the universe could not have been created in-the-first-place.

Birnbaum posits both an eternal dynamic (Infinite Potential) and a cosmic purpose (the quest for Infinite Potential) while Spinoza develops neither of these major issues. Birnbaum is acutely aware of the apparent major gaps in Spinozan Determinism, but only obliquely notes that deficit.

The extraordinary works and lives of Spinoza and Birnbaum converge and diverge on major conceptual areas. In the 'convergence' department both believe that everything spanning the cosmic order is interconnected – past, present and future; both believe that a transcendent lattice-work unifies all life; both believe that an overarching force drives the cosmic order; and both very clearly leave open the metaphysical possibility of describing this force ultimately as God.

There are interesting parallels in their life sagas as well. Each writes as an aside to their respective secular professions; each writes to a world audience; each has deep scholarship in the historic field; each has erudition in-depth in the myriad Jewish philosophical and mystical sources; each crafted an original philosophical paradigm; each introduce their ideas relatively early in life; each declined teaching positions in philosophy; and both believe in the treatise-form as the ideal 'teaching modality.'

While each, in his own way, proposes a total philosophical revolution – the two theories are conceptually radically different. Spinoza's universe is cold and deterministic, devoid of freedom; Birnbaum's universe is rich and organic, a vibrant universe of maximum Potential and freedom.

Birnbaum asserts that his core philosophical paradigm can be employed by the spectrum of mankind: archetypes Religious Man, Spiritual Man and Secular Man. Humans, as an expression of Infinite Potential and the divine, have the freedom to choose their own expression of their Potentiality. This leads to a central tenet of Potentialism: Mankind has Free Will.

Spinoza's Determinism is something quite different, asserting that people are led by their own hard-wired emotions and that those emotions were put in place by God. Spinoza states that active, strong emotions cannot be overcome by reason, only by stronger emotions. In that way we are products of the universe, directly and inexorably guided by our God-given desires. According to Determinism, mankind does not truly have Free Will.

Likewise, Birnbaum and Spinoza disagree on the nature of evil. To Birnbaum, Evil is real. In a cosmos predicated on Potential, however, it cannot be countered by an intervening God. In contrast, Spinoza asserts Evil is not real; it just appears that way for lack of understanding.

Interestingly, concepts of both Spinoza's Ethics (c. 1677) and Birnbaum's Summa Metaphysica (first volume 1988) are later present in Programming the Universe (2006), a book by 'outlier' MIT Professor of Quantum Mechanics Seth Lloyd. Lloyd believes that the universe is like a super quantum computer. His concepts are highly complementary to Birnbaum's interlaced and perpetually iterating universe. In fact, Birnbaum's Quest for Potential theory (1988) nicely sets the conceptual stage for the Lloyd's quantum computing universe in which the universe is constantly self-iterating and evolving, as well.

Birnbaum notes vis à vis Lloyd - "While the cosmos may appear to have been mechanistic in its early stages, its ongoing work-in-progress goal is far from mechanistic. The universe sets-the-stage for – and proactively seeks – optimization of the multiplicity of venues and dimensions, including the aesthetic and emotional and possibly the spiritual... The mechanistic aspect of our universe is necessary but not sufficient. The mechanics are but a platform or base from which Quest for Potential advances forth, pressing the iterative limits of extraordinariation."

In November 2013, erudite British journalist Oliver Burkeman, echoing the iconic French anthropologist Claude Levi-Strauss (2006) described Birnbaum's metaphysics as "remarkable and profound" (and as "not unscientific"). Similarly, University of Maine Professor of Biology and Ecology Andrei Alyokhin, in November 2012, forthrightly endorses the theory: "David Birnbaum's Summa Metaphysica is a major philosophical contribution to the study of Being...Summa represents a bold attempt to formulate a unifying concept of the Universe......it is reasonable to propose the Quest for Potential as a working hypothesis for explaining the impetus behind the cosmic dynamic."

Spinoza and Birnbaum are paradigm-breaking philosophers who have shaped the study of philosophy. Both their works can be found in university classrooms across the country and the world – from UCLA on the West Coast to Yeshiva University and Brandeis on the East Coast to Hebrew University in Jerusalem.

Built from a history of thinking, communicating, extrapolating, and creative thinking, the working hypothesis Quest for Potential∞ is a radical departure from Determinism. This newly-proposed concept is not unlikely to serve as a very key building block for future levels of understanding. Potentialism marks a seminal point of philosophical advance; it is a paradigm challenge of the first order.

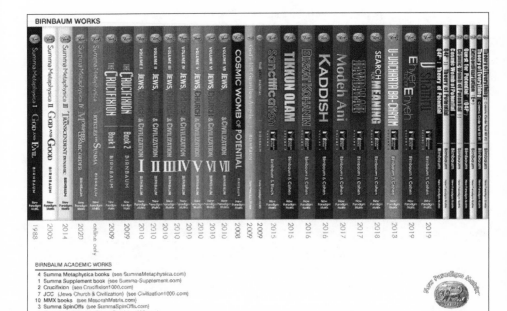

BIRNBAUM ACADEMIC WORKS

4 Summa Metaphysica books (see SummaMetaphysica.com)
1 Summa Supplement book (see Summa-Supplement.com)
2 Crucifixion (see Crucifixion1000.com)
7 JCC (Jews Church & Civilization) (see Civilization1000.com)
10 MMX books (see MesorahMatrix.com)
3 Summa SpinOffs (see SummaSpinOffs.com)
8 Theory graphics (see TheoryGraphics1000.com)
35 (updated: 10.12.21)

I believe I have-the-edge

So, I am a solitary conceptual theorist -
with metaphysics as a passion;
It is not my 'day job'
- although I have diligently worked on its conceptualization since age 10
(1960) and then its exposition (starting with Summa I) since1988
- including through my time in Cambridge, MASS - while at Harvard grad
school (1972-4);
I have lived and breathed the field for 60+ years.

Arrayed against me in metaphysics/cosmology/philosophy is a 'British
Empire'-wide cohort
headquartered in an iconic British university - and peppered throughout
many stellar British universities, in particular -
with many mobilized to sideline and undermine me
- at every turn along-the-way
via severe and ongoing *ad hominem* attacks
and other ongoing subterfuge

I am, however, quite confident that my metaphysics - Potentialism -
will prevail.
Potentialism Theory radically trumps the opposition's (alleged)
metaphysics - Randomness - which I respectfully view as vacuous,
and which I respectfully label - *a theory of no theory.*

Randomness is, respectfully,
   The Emperor's Clothes
     - on a grand scale

Radomness Theory is an *'echo chamber* of vacuousness' - on steroids;

Randomness can readily be confused with a Fundamentalist fanatic
   religious cult -
   fact-free, yet hell-bent on debasing and undermining all 'non-believers'

Randomness makes ALCHEMY look like *hard science*;

Respectfully, I *have-the-edge* on the ultimate chessboard
because I have, respectfully, conceptualized a radically superior

>

because I have, respectfully, conceptualized a radically superior metaphysics -
which is substantive, unified, covers-the-bases, and is quite fully vetted.

Potentialism Theory works - on every level,
Randomness Theory does not work on any level.

The opposing cohort, the Random Universe crew -
outguns me at least 100,000 to 1 for sure -
However, it has no *authentic* cards to play;
- only the *toxic cards* of character assassination, and related

One can readily make-the-case
*that the 'opposition's **vocal attack-cadre**, in particular, is*
*   **intellectually and morally bankrupt***

1) the Randomnists still have a modicum of power and status on the
   academic chessboard -
   but no real theory
2) Thus to preserve their status and power, they simply bludgeon any
   opposing theorists
3) The Randomnists play by *academic gangster rules*
4) They have perfected the art of *debasement and invalidation*
5) With no authentic intellectual argument, the group has turned to
   neo-criminal gambits -
   to slander, undermine, debase & defame

The Brits bet that the world is dumb.

*

I bet that the world is smart.

Science is driven by vibrant debate and search-for-truth -
and, indeed, by revolution, as appropriate

- not by a toxic mixture of nihilism and British jingoism
  masquerading as *science*

"there is no comparable volume...
comprehensive, authoritative, intelligible...
... a remarkable effort to offer a fresh approach"

POTENTIALISM THEORY

- Prof of Philosophy Paul Mendes-Flohr [on Summa I]
Hebrew University, Jerusalem
Editor, *20th Century Jewish Religious Thought*

"the best book in print on the subject"
[theodicy]

POTENTIALISM THEORY

- Heritage Journal
on Summa I
[God and Evil]

"a great intellectual and spiritual work"

POTENTIALISM THEORY

Joseph Dan, Professor of Kabbalah
Hebrew University, Jerusalem
[on Summa I]

"Seven centuries after Thomas Aquinas's
Summa Theologica, *David Birnbaum offers his*
landmark metaphysics, Summa Metaphysica"

POTENTIALISM THEORY

-Theological Studies / Georgetown University
[on Summa I]

THE ULTIMATE POWER

POTENTIALISM THEORY

IS, AFTER ALL, *HIDING IN PLAIN SIGHT*

MORPHED COSMIC ORDER

Section O

MORPHED COSMIC ORDER

Essentially, Q4P$^\infty$ maneuvers & thrusts-for >

POTENTIALISM THEORY

the fullest possible *Self-Actualization* of the universe

HUMANS, LIKE THE UNIVERSE

POTENTIALISM THEORY

ARE **HYBRID** PHYSICAL/METAPHYSICAL

in-the-mix, Birnbaum's Evolution theory >

POTENTIALISM THEORY

displaces Darwin's Evolution theory

Birnbaum commits 5 *high crimes* against British academe

POTENTIALISM THEORY

His theory (fatally) undermines that of British home-town favorite Darwin
He is a Directional Universe Theorist; not a Randomness Theorist
He is Harvard; not Cambridge U
His theory is bulletproof; unlike *bizarro* Brit Theory-of-No-Theory Randomness
He is not a sworn hard-line Atheist

WE ARE POTENTIAL

POTENTIALISM THEORY

IN HUMAN FORM

POTENTIAL IS ETERNAL - *BY DEFINITION*

POTENTIALISM THEORY

THE AXIOM IS *SELF-EVIDENT*

re. Summa Metaphysica I (1988)

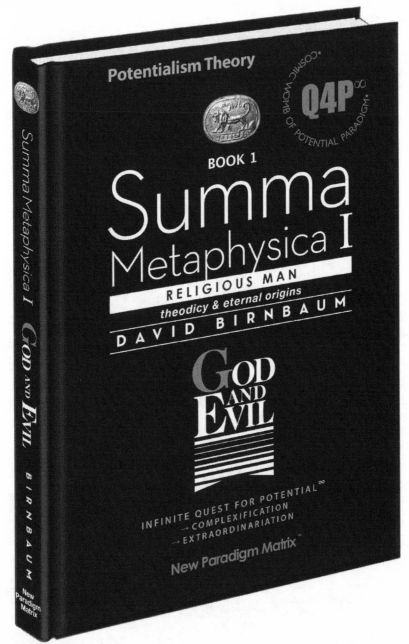

selected excerpts from book flap

Summa Metaphysica I
GOD AND EVIL

by DAVID BIRNBAUM

David Birnbaum's God and Evil is a major philosophical study which systematically confronts the philosophical problem of evil, and the Holocaust in particular...

Summa Metaphysica I: God and Evil: Religious Man (1988) is the first of three books in Birnbaum's landmark three-volume Summa Metaphysica series crafted over a twenty-six year period...

In Book #1 of the series, Birnbaum introduces the concepts of Quest for Potential∞ (Q4P∞), as well as God of Potential...

According to Birnbaum's paradigm, Quest for Potential∞ drives Man and God/god and the Cosmos. Potential is the nexus. God of Potential is juxtaposed against Man of Autonomy-Freedom-Potential...

Combining modern and classic, rationalist and mystic themes...

The Summa series reshapes the contours of metaphysics, philosophy, and theology.

NEW JERSEY

David.Birnbaum.NY@gmail.com

re. Summa Metaphysica I (1988)

THE GOD OF POTENTIAL

Eheyeh

As noted, a key Biblcal name of God
Self-identified at The 'Burning Bush' saga
c. 1250 BCE exodus from Egypt
- Book of Exodus [*Shemot*] 3:14 is -
(in the Biblical hebrew) *Eheyeh Asher Eheye*h
"I WILL BE THAT WHICH I WILL BE"

I AM THE GOD OF POTENTIAL

And, if the Divine
is the God of Potential
then THEODICY (the problem of evil)
and THEOGONY (the origins of the Divine)
both fall into place philosophically

See Summa I: God and Evil: Religious Man
for elucidation

re. Summa Metaphysica I (1988)

a focused YouTube channel

Unifying Science & Spirituality

a video review of Potentialism Theory

by Benjamin Blech

www.UnifyingScienceSpirituality.com

re. Summa Metaphysica I (1988)

God and Evil *respectfully* proposes an original[**]
and *simultaneous solution* to the key inter-related classic problems
in philosophy/metaphysics/theology.

THEOGONY –
The "origins" of the Infinite Divine
or more broadly, of the Primal Force of the cosmos,
if such exists

COSMOLOGY –
The "origins", evolution, structure and prime dynamics
of the cosmos

THEODICY –
The classic *Problem of Evil*:
If there is a God who is all-powerful and all-merciful,
why is there (gross) evil

TELEOLOGY –
The purpose/end-goal of the universe and existence
(if indeed, there is *purpose*)

[**]note: The original God and Evil copyright by David Birnbaum was 1986.

Holy Divine Potential.....
the infinite Divine blaze leapt forth....

"Independent of time, matter, and energy, and indeed, independent of a universe, existed Holy Divine Potential—the primordial Divine. At the eternal origins of out-of-time: Holy Potential within potential within potential *ad infinitum*—tracking to the forward edges of time.

At the embryonic stage of holiness, deep in the womb of nothingness, deep at the core of out-of-time, hinged on an indefinable and infinite circularity, there was an ascending holy metaphysical fire: Yearning, imploring, calling forth into the void.

[The concept of a primordial Divine has clear and direct precedent in the concept of the *En Sof* of Kabbalah.]

Traversing the Bridge
And as nature abhors a vacuum, Holy Potential abhors nothingness. This is a cosmic axiom.

Simultaneous with the eternal origins of out-of-time, an equilibrium of nothingness was thrown into disequilibrium by its own Holy Potential. Exploding and imploding. Echoing through this day and racing towards infinite time, Holy Potential screamed forth.

Genesis
Flowing from the Essence of the Divine, the infinite holy potential of the Divine demanded more expression. Among these elements were the potentials for creation of the universe, and within the latter the potentials for man to quest for his spiritual potential, as well as others, including mercy, love, truth, justice, beauty, and harmony. The holy potential core of the Divine demanded more than just potential. For the potentialities of Divine creation are inherent in the eternal Divine origins and in the Divine Essence itself.

At the eye of the primal cosmic storm, warping from out-of-time towards time, unzipping the cosmic void into positives and negatives, the infinite Divine blaze leapt forth. A creative supraconscious dynamic, transcending time, space, and eternity. Focusing its holy metaphysical force. Genesis.

and God divided the light from the darkness.

—Genesis 1:4

A holy dynamic flows forth through this day, tracing its origins to the inner core of the Divine. Beneath the eddies and swirls at the surface of the cosmic stream, beneath the deep and powerful major cosmic currents, from out of the epicenter of the holy, flows the deepest primal current—questing, beseeching, and indeed, screaming—for ultimate potentiality.**"**

re. Summa Metaphysica I (1988)

PRAISE FOR SUMMA I - **God and Evil**

"MASTERPIECE"

- **AJHS**
  Heritage Journal
  New York

- **Nahum N. Glatzer**
  Boston University

- **Dr. Sanford Drob**
  Founder, NY Jewish Review

- **Professor William Johnson**
  Brandeis University

- **Rabbi Benjamin Blech**
  Yeshiva University

- **Professor Masako Nakagawa**
  Villanova University

see www.Summa-1.com

"A Major Work in the Philosophy of Religion"*

"...there is no comparable volume offering such a comprehensive, authoritative and intelligible discussion of the problem... a remarkable effort to offer a fresh approach."

> Paul Mendes-Flohr, Professor of Philosophy, Hebrew University, Jerusalem, Editor, *Contemporary Jewish Religious Thought*

"...an original, and, in this reader's opinion, a very promising point of view... the author gathers a philosophically coherent and, in the end, highly modern insight... a unified metaphysics..."

> Louis Dupré, Professor of Religious Studies, Yale University

"...a major work in the Philosophy of Religion...a masterful achievement...a novel and satisfying approach... a major intellectual achievement."

> *Cannon William Johnson, Professor of Philosophy, Brandeis University

"...a major contribution to the Jewish conversations through the ages, on theodicy, and the problem of evil generally."

> Dr. Norman Lamm, President, Yeshiva University

"David Birnbaum brings the rich resources of the Jewish tradition to bear on the universal problem of theodicy. The result is a new synthesis... I can certainly recommend it as a fascinating contribution to the philosophy of religion which merits the attention of Christians and Jews alike."

> John J. Collins, Professor of Theology, University of Notre Dame Editor, *Journal of Biblical Literature*

"*God and Evil* represents a bold attempt to formulate an ingenious theory, which, drawing upon creative reinterpretations of classical Jewish doctrine, places the Free Will Defense within a broader metaphysical framework..."

> Rabbi Walter S. Wurzburger, Professor of Philosophy, Yeshiva University, Editor, *Tradition*

"All who read this book will find much instruction, insight, and material for reflection...I find the overall thesis of the book touching and inspiring..."

> Rabbi Irving Greenberg, President, The National Jewish Center for Learning and Scholarship (CLAL)

"A major work...a great intellectual and spiritual effort"

> Joseph Dan, Professor of Kabbalah, Hebrew University

re. Summa Metaphysica I (1988)

NY Jewish Review

The New Kabbalah

"David Birnbaum's God and Evil is a bold and highly original synthesis which attempts to provide an overarching metaphysical solution to the vexing problem of radical evil in a world created and sustained by an all powerful, all knowing, benevolent God. Birnbaum's treatment of the highly intimidating and emotionally wrenching problem of a Jewish theodicy in a post-Holocaust world is audacious yet sensitive, traditional and yet highly innovative."

"The closer mankind comes to fulfilling his spiritual, intellectual and other potentials, the closer he comes to fulfilling his purpose on earth via his role as a partner with God in creation. In doing so, however, man must maximize his privacy, independence and freedom. As mankind then moves closer to its own self-actual-ization, God must, of necessity, retreat further and further into "eclipse." Mankind has, over the centuries, indeed ascended greatly in knowledge, implicitly demanding greater and greater freedom. For God to intervene directly in human affaires at this late stage in mankind's development, as he did, for example, for the Jews in Egypt, would reverse the very development of both His and mankind's essence, and Birnbaum's terms, threaten to 'unravel the cosmos.'"

Sanford Drob
Editor-in-Chief
NY Jewish Review
February 1990
The Lurianic

Kabbalah is treated in detail in Sanford Drob's Symbols of the Kabbalah and Kabbalistic Metaphors .

see www.NewKabbalah.com

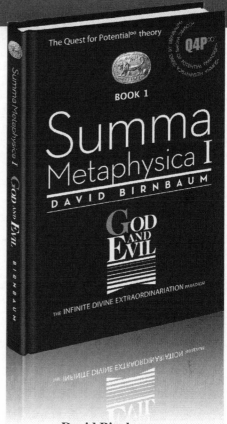

Recommended reading:

Theological Aspects of the Holocaust

THE SIMON WIESENTHAL CENTER

The Simon Wiesenthal Center is a global Jewish human rights organization that confronts anti-Semitism, hate and terrorism, promotes human rights and dignity, stands with Israel, defends the safety of Jews worldwide, and teaches the lessons of the Holocaust for future generations. With a constituency of over 400,000 households in the United States, it is accredited as an NGO at international organizations including the United Nations, UNESCO, OSCE, Organization of American States (OAS), the Latin American Parliament (PARLATINO) and the Council of Europe.

David Birnbaum
1989
God and Evil:
A Unified Theodicy/Theology/Philosophy

Museum of Tolerance **ONLINE**
MULTIMEDIA LEARNING CENTER
Beit Hashoah

www.wiesenthal.com

re. Summa Metaphysica I (1988)

UNIFYING SCIENCE & SPIRITUALITY

To the secular,
mechanistic
Infinite Quest for Potential.

To the spiritual,
the metaphysical/spiritual
Infinite Quest for Potential.

To the religious,
the Holy
Infinite Divine Potential.

Eheyeh Asher Eheyeh:
I Will Be That Which I Will Be (Book of Exodus 3:14)
The Infinite Divine. Shadai. The Source. Holy Quest for Potential
The kabbalistic En Sof ('The No-End')

Secular, Spiritual or Holy, the grand cosmic journey of Potential
advances-onward to this day.

With Freedom - axiomatically integral to Potential - being
consequently inviolate, as well.
(This 'axiomatic play' is integral to Summa's proposed resolution of
the classic Theodicy connundrum.)

David Birnbaum Summa Metaphysica philosophy treatise proposes a unified metaphysics | cosmology | teleology.

In the process Birnbaum *sets the stage* for a reboot of all the hard and soft sciences.

***

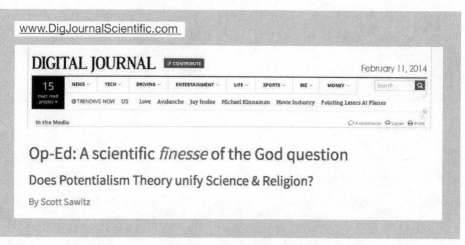

re. Summa Metaphysica I (1988)

Book of the Year
1989

(Summa I)

pegging-off of Summa I section 400.20
Updated focus on the 0-point

EVIL

So, why is there Evil at all?

I form the light, and create darkness;
I make peace, and create evil; I am the Lord,
Who has made all these things.

- Isaiah 45:5

Evil has its source in the good.

- Augustine

*

At eternal origins, there was just the 0-point.

At some point
Potential split 0 into -

Positives and Negatives,
Pluses and Minuses,
Matter and anti-Matter,
Good and Evil

MORPHED COSMIC ORDER

re. Summa Metaphysica I (1988)

To ignite a universe,
one must split 0

And if one splits 0,
there will thus of necessity
be Evil
in the mix

*

There would apparently
simply be no way
to create or update the universe
with no Evil in it;

Else, that would have been
The Plan
in the first place

*

Do you insist on No Evil?
Then, No universe.

Do you wish a universe?
Then Evil will
be an actor.

*

The concept of the primordial 0 being split into PLUSES
and MINUSES has resonance, whether from esoteric
ancient strains, through Summa Metaphysica I (1988),
and then through contemporary (21st Century) Quantum
Mechanics.

See "IT from BIT" (1990) theoretical physics hypothesis
of Princeton's iconic John Wheeler (1911-2008), and
developed via his intellectual heir, MIT's Quantum
guru Seth Lloyd. See, in particular, Lloyd's (seminal)
Programming the Universe, 2006, Knopf. See in further
focus Lloyd's Chapter 3: The Computational Universe
(subsection: The Story of the Universe).

*

So, in 2006 Lloyd's quantum mechanics 21st Century
physics fortuitously makes an appearance just after
Summa Metaphysica II (2005) and Summa Metaphysica I
(1988); his work buttress aspects of Potentialsm Theory's
metaphysics (theodicy and Eternal Origins components).

*

more theological texture

The midrash (Jewish exegesis, parable and lore)
has the (omnipotent) Divine
weeping over Evil

Thus, a Divine not quite "omnipotent"
and not quite
impervious to Evil & suffering

re. Summa Metaphysica I (1988)

more excerpts

excerpts from
God and Evil (Summa Metaphysica I)
KTAV Publishing, NJ, 1988,
from section 300:00: The Underlying Dynamic
pps. 78-82

THE UNDERLYING COSMIC DYNAMIC

" Holy quest for potential is the underlying core dynamic of the cosmic order.

Holy quest for potential—our parallel to the kabbalistic *En Sof*—is the "primal scream" of the cosmos...

Holy Potential, emanating through and from the Divine essence, radiates through the universe—questing, pulsating, exploding, reaching, energizing, expanding, in time and out-of-time...

It is at the core of the holy/natural drive of the cosmos. It is the primal engine of cosmic existence.

*

The Genesis Point: From there on through this day the majesty of creation seeks its maximal potential.

Life is daring. The cosmos strives not just for survival; it quests for its maximal potential...

continued

Long before Prometheus stole fire from the gods to give
to man, God grasped life from out of the void and created fire
and man.

*

The universe seeks its maximum and optimal potential—
inexorably. For this, we postulate, is its *raison d'être.*

*

"Holy Potentiality" is a thoroughly overarching dynamic,
emanating from the infinitely holy through creation to the far
reaches of the cosmic order. Soloveitchik notes: "He is the
Lord of the hosts, who resides in every infinitessimal particle
of creation and the whole universe is replete with His glory."

*

At the Genesis Point, a Divine spark leapt forth. The
spark initiates a cycle of becoming, creation, and rebirth.
It is the core of this spiritual blaze of potentiality whose
ultimate perfect achievement is a primal cosmic end. It is this
transcendental flame which directly continues the spark of Life
which the Divine infused through Primal Man.

*

The cosmic thrust for potential is man-centered. Within
this constraint, the cosmos seeks its own perfection. The
quests for spirituality and perfection, and the attendant quests
for freedom, harmony, and beauty find their source in the
metaphysical spark which actualized the cosmos. It was the
origin of this quest of quests which bridged the gap from
"nothingness" to "Somethingness."

"

David.Birnbaum.NY@gmail.com

re. Summa Metaphysica I (1988)

This New Paradigm Matrix work

is available via multiple modalities:

amazon: www.AmazonX1000.com

eBooks: www.eReader1000.com

online: www.SummaMetaphysica.com

contact: NPM1000@yahoo.com

Additional High-level Testimonials

"David Birnbaum has woven together motifs from both rationalists and mystics...absorbing and impressive."
David Shatz, Professor of Philosophy
Yeshiva University, New York, NY

"a highly original and imaginative synthesis... Written with lucidity and deep conviction this book will prove highly stimulating to the layman and the scholar."
Joseph Schultz, Professor of Judaic Studies
University of Missouri, Columbia, MO

"David Birnbaum has opened up a new avenue of approach...novel hypothesis clearly and attractively presented...a remarkably informed study... It is a very impressive piece of work which should provoke considerable discussion and debate."
Donald Gray, Professor of Religious Studies
Manhattan College, New York, NY

"important and original... It proposes a new solution to the age-old problem of the existence of evil in the world. The approach Birnbaum takes can be applied not only to Judaism but to religious philosophy in general. I am particularly impressed by the author's grappling with the most difficult issues facing contemporary religious thought in a lucid and perceptive manner."
Lawrence Schiffman, Professor of Hebrew and Judaic Studies
New York University, NY

"...a challenging new hypothesis...compelling...intellectually stimulating. It took me back again to my Roman Catholic seminary studies of Aquinas. I felt again the pull of great ideas, the struggles of Masters grappling with Mysteries...respectful of the past while carefully positing new positions... His solution deserves to be given serious consideration..."
Gerard A. Vanderhaar, Professor of Religion and Peace Studies
Catholic Brothers College, Memphis, TN

MORPHED COSMIC ORDER

re. Summa Metaphysica I (1988)

"...author and scholar David Birnbaum does what has eluded the greatest minds and thinkers ...looks at the evidence from a genuinely fresh and original perspective ...his brilliant thesis is built upon solid foundations of impeccable scholarship."
    Rabbi A. Mark Levin, Anshe Sphard Congregation
    Christian Brothers College, Memphis TN

"...powerful and original ...a conceptual breakthrough in theological philosophical thought ...God and Evil is not an incremental advance over existing theological thought. It is a quantum leap, and presents a new universal theological underpinning ...the book has a potential for greatness."
    Rabbi Marvin Tokayer, Senior Rabbi
    Jewish Community of Japan

"a truly stimulating and creative contribution to the post-Shoah discussion ...overall direction is one that I find extremely promising ... I believe it is the only sensible way to proceed ... What is especially appealing about this volume is its ability to draw together new insights and the wisdom of the tradition in a creative synthesis."
    John T. Pawlikowski, Professor of Social Ethics
    M.A. Director, Catholic Theological Union
    Member, U.S. Holocaust Memorial Commission
    Chicago, IL

"...researched extensively, presented in a scholarly manner and creative in thesis ...a theodicy/theology/philosophy which maintains its internal consistency and which provides a framework
within which to find the answers ...courageously ventures into new territory ...must be admired for its originality, its logical consistency and its courage"
    Rabbi Dale Polakoff
    Great Neck Synagogue, NY

"Birnbaum addresses the subject with an originality of approach which is wholly his own, and is bound to stir the minds of his readers. Although the works is essentially that of a Jew conducting his enquiry from the standpoint of Jewish religious thought, students of other faiths, lay and clerical, too will find the volume sustaining long-asked questions and challenging longheld beliefs."

Isaac L. Swift, Rabbi Emeritus
Congregation Ahavath Torah, Englewood, NJ

"I have read GOD and EVIL with interest and profit. It is a searching, knowledgeable, and readable attempt to confront the fundamental moral problem of theodicy with its most severe contemporary test, that of the Holocaust."

Berel Lang, Professor of Philosophy and Humanistic Studies
Chairman, Department of Philosophy
State University of New York at Albany

"Mr. Birnbaum has bravely entered into the vast fields of theodicy, an intellectual and spiritual terrain usually known for its complexity, difficulty and obscurity. GOD and EVIL represents a new, unflinching, yet reverential attempt to orient the events of history... With an evident intellectual daring, Birnbaum is not content to merely defend God...a fascinating, original and provocative reformulation of medieval Lurianic Kabbalah... It is a solution which will stimulate Jew and Christian alike."

Richard A. Cohen, Associate Professor of Philosophy
Shawnee State University, Portsmouth, OH

"...an intellectually engaging work. Birnbaum's relentless inquiry and probing approach to the issue of theodicy offer the reader an adventure of ideas... I recommend the book highly."

Rabbi William E. Kaufman
Temple Beth El, Fall River, MA
Visiting Professor of Philosophy
Rhode Island College, Providence, RI

MORPHED COSMIC ORDER

"...a masterpiece for our times..."
Benjamin Blech, Rabbi, Young Israel of Oceanside
Author, "Theodicy" tape series
New York, NY

"...is sure to be regarded as a major contribution to the Jewish study of theodicy...the first major theological study that systematically confronts this problem directly and in detail... All subsequent work on the presence of evil in this world will have to take seriously this book and the cogent and direct analysis it brings to the topic."
Peter J. Haas, Associate Professor of Jewish Literature and Thought
Vanderbilt University, Nashville, TN

"This book accomplishes a remarkable feature. It manages to provide a theodicy within the framework of traditional Jewish belief and philosophy and not only a theodicy which works, but which does so with intellectual rigor and emotional satisfaction. The intellectual honesty and emotional sensitivity are apparent on every page."
Professor David M. Goldenberg, Associate Director
Annenberg Research Institute, Philadelphia, PA

"David Birnbaum's engrossing book God and Evil is a highly informed discussion of the perennial problem of theodicy. Steeped in Jewish learning, it is a strikingly original midrash on a very difficult theme, written with a boldness and passion, and is a pleasure to read..."
David Winston, Professor of Hellenistic and Judaic Studies
Graduate Theological Union, Berkeley, CA

"God and Evil is an engaging and thoughtful work. It brings a fresh new approach to an old problem, utilizing classical Jewish and other sources in a dynamic, compelling and creative manner.... As a person who has spent many years dealing with the problem of theodicy, I must confess that I approached your book with skepticism. I thought that all that could be said, had been said. Nevertheless, I was surprised at what I learned from your work. Thank you for writing it."
Dr. Byron L. Sherwin, Vice-President for Academic Affairs
Spertus College of Judaica, Chicago, IL

Potentialism Theory = Summa Theory = Birnbaum Theory = Q4P Theory = Quantum Man Theory

Summa Metaphysica by David Birnbaum

Course Text grid
Summa I and/or Summa II and/or Summa III

	Institution	City	Course Name	Professor
	BRANDEIS UNIVERSITY	Waltham, MA	Advanced Religious Philosophy	William Johnson
	EMORY UNIVERSITY	Atlanta, GA	Post-Holocaust Jewish Theology	Michael Berger
	GRATZ COLLEGE	Melrose Park, PA	Post-Holocaust Theology	Moshe Shner
	GRESHAM COLLEGE	London, United Kingdom	Comparative Religion, Philosophy of Religion	Gwen Griffith-Dickson
	HARDING UNIVERSITY	Memphis, TN	Providence & Suffering	Douglas Brown
	HARTFORD SEMINARY	Hartford, CT	Suffering, Theodicy, and Repentance and Spiritual Transformation	Yehezkel Landau
	HEBREW UNIVERSITY	Jerusalem, Israel	Contemporary Jewish Philosophy	Eliezer Schweid
	JEWISH THEOLOGICAL SEMINARY	New York, New York	Philosophy: Evil	Ed Greenstein
	REGIS UNIVERSITY	Denver, CO	Philosophy: Understanding Evil	Lester L. Bundy
	STETSON UNIVERSITY	Deland, FL	The Problem of Evil	Donald W. Musser
	UCLA	Los Angeles, CA	Modern Religious Jewish Thought	David Winston
	UNION THEOLOGICAL SEMINARY	New York, New York	Foundations in Christian Theology	James H. Cone
	UNIVERSITY OF WALES	Cardiff, Wales, United Kingdom	Jewish Studies	Dan Cohn-Sherbok
	UNIVERSITY OF WINDSOR	Ontario, Canada	Theology and Philosophy of Religion	Barry Whitney
	YESHIVA UNIVERSITY	New York, New York	Jewish Philosophy	David Shatz

note: The logo representation is, of course, not an institutional endorsement of the Summa Metaphysica philosophical paradigm by the respective colleges/seminaries

re. Summa Metaphysica I (1988)

"the best book in print on the subject"
—HERITAGE JOURNAL

"Author and scholar David Birbaum wrestles with the age-old problem of the existence of evil... a compelling, stimulating and creative contribution..."
—JUDAICA BOOK NEWS

"Birnbaum's God and Evil is an extremely significant volume which grapples forthrightly and originally with the problem... well-organized... clearly written... persuasive... Birnbaum comes as close as possible to solving the awesome dilemma of evil in a world created by a just God."
—JEWISH WORLD

"Birnbaum wrestles with the problem of evil from a Jewish perspective, but provides fresh insights for Christians as well. This is a good book, written in faith, and with honesty and passion... Birnbaum's Summa Metphysica is powerfully juxtaposed against Aquinas' Summa Theologica"
—THEOLOGICAL STUDIES
   Georgetown University

"Wiesel and Birnbaum share a deep respect for, and loyalty to, their ancestral faith. Yet the contrast between their approaches is ultimately perhaps as instructive as the approaches themselves. Birnbaum's approach is essentially that of the intellectual, philosopher, and theologian..."
—CANADIAN CATHOLIC REVIEW

"a bold and highly original synthesis... audacious yet sensitive, traditional and yet highly innovative... yet within the parameters of an aithentically jewish halakhic point of view... an intellectual oddyssey"
—JEWISH REVIEW

"meticulously argued, impeccable researched... an excellent work of immense value."
—EXPOSITORY TIMES
   London

MORPHED COSMIC ORDER

Section P

MORPHED COSMIC ORDER

A hyper-aggressive cadre of British jingoists
rabidly attacks theorists diverging from Darwin -
and Directional Universe theorists, in particular

POTENTIALISM THEORY

However, via their ongoing toxic tactics,
the cadre ends-up debasing 'British honor'
- and the British brand/legacy

"RIDE BOLDLY, RIDE,
THE SHADE REPLIED

POTENTIALISM THEORY

IF YOU SEEK FOR ELDORADO"
- EDGAR ALAN POE, Eldorado

---

the metaphysical/physical STARSHIP

POTENTIALISM THEORY

Organic Proactive Supercomputer Super--Organism

In-the-mix

POTENTIALISM THEORY

upholds Aristotle's (d. 322 BCE) Directional Universe [teleology] thrust
does a very major overhaul of Kabbalist Luria's (d. 1572 BCE) En Sof [No End]
displaces Darwin's (d.1882) Random Mutation & Natural Selection thrusts
seamlessly wraps-around Einstein's (d. 1955) iconic Macro Physics formula (1905)
lays the metaphysical framework for Wheeler's (d. 2008) 'It from Bit' (1990) proposition
lays the metaphysical framework for Seth Lloyd (b.1960) of MIT's quantum
    computer universe physics proposition (2006) [in Programming the Universe]
delivers-on Nobel laureate Leon Lederman's (d. 2018) T-Shirt **formula** request (1984)

AN AUTHENTIC GRAND PHILOSOPHY

POTENTIALISM THEORY

A **NEW PARADIGM** METAPHYSICS

MORPHED COSMIC ORDER

a unified metaphysics

We draw your attention to the following "verdict" almost three decades-ago on Summa I from the iconic Dupré, noted authority on – and arbiter of - proposed "new paradigm metaphysics" offerings –

"an original and in this reader's opinion, very promising point of view....the author gathers a philosophically coherent and, in the end, highly modern insight...He appropriately describes it as a unified metaphysics within the constraints of Jewish doctrine, consistent with its historical development, and consistent with secular scientific thought..."

– Louis Dupré, Professor of Religious Studies, Yale University (1989)*

* original letter copy is posted on the www.Philosophy1000.com site under icon **Review Letters.**

7 CRITERIA

Academia.edu   click >> **www.7criteria.com**

DOC   A

The 7 Criteria for a Great Metaphysics: David Birnbaum's Elegant Philosophy Paradigm

The 7 Criteria for a Great Metaphysics: David Birnbaum's Elegant Philosophy Paradigm

UPLOADED BY
Mark Davis

CONNECT TO DOWNLOAD

8+ GET DOC   f   ✉

6 Pages

[the Birnbaum]

TELEOLOGY [*a,*b]

formula / direction / purpose / path
of the universe

$$Q4P^\infty > C+ > E+ \qquad {}^{*c}$$

[wrapping-around the Einstein formula] [*d]

NO FLAW HAS BEEN DISCERNED [*e]

*a https://en.wikipedia.org/wiki/Teleology

*b *aka* the Birnbaum Super-Formula

*c see Direction1000.com

*d see Einstein1000.com

*e see HuffPost1000.com

Potentialism-Summa.com

REPRISE

Quick Overview

The Proposed Working Hypothesis

Potentialism Theory hypothesizes that if we introduce one (conceptualized) metaphysical concept - Quest for Potential∞ - as the eternal *'driver'* of the Cosmic Order, then entire inter-related clusters of hitherto unresolved issues across science, religion, metaphysics and philosophy - including (but not limited to) cosmology, cosmogony, theogony, theodicy, teleology and evolutionary biology - are all simultaniously lanced.

The fusion of my Potentialism Theory - with MIT LLoyd's (information communication & computation) quantum mechanics - provides a quite-powerful proposition: A seamless A-Z metaphysics/physics/cosmology. Sort of what many people have been seeking for a long time.

A well-vetted and quite-possibly correct simultaneous solution - a fully integrated,all-embracing metaphysics / new paradigm - is perhaps something worth evaluating. One concept (Quest for Potential∞) resolving conundrums across a dozen+ fields? If essentially on the mark, it would indeed transform the world as we know it.

That is what SummaMetaphysica/Potentialism has proposed - starting with the focus on theodicy in Summa I: God and Evil in 1988.

All data-points vector towards the theory being correct. After 28+ years of public vetting, not a single flaw has been discerned in it. And as we know from 7th grade mathematics, elegant possible *simultaneous solutions* inevitably have a way of turning out to be correct.

Potentialism proposes that our universe indeed has a direction (Quest for Potential∞). Advocates of an aimless and random universe have been having a public nervous breakdown over the theory since God and Evil (Summa I) was published by KTAV twenty-eight years - and six printings - ago in 1988.

Potentialism Theory is, as well, simple yet powerful (i.e. infinitely nested). And indeed, to add irony to the potentially pivotal theory, its proposed *key to the cosmic code* - Quest for Potential∞ - has always been 'hiding in plain sight'.

The theory can be viewed through a religious lens (see Summa Metaphysica I: God and Evil); a spiritual lens (see Summa Metaphysica II: God and Good) or a secular lens (see Summa Metaphysica III: The Transcendent Dynamic).   >>>

MORPHED COSMIC ORDER

The theory shatters various 'idols' along the way. The world is not *flat*, nor is the universe *random* - by any means. The universe may be far more dynamic and fully-integrated than hitherto suspected, to put matters mildly.

Various entrenched 'priesthoods' - whether in academe or otherwise - will *diss* any truly threatening paradigm - and will fight rearguard battles, sometimes vicious ones, to protect their power prerogatives. But these reactionary efforts against a formidable new paradigm will ultimately fail.

The Random Universe formulation is simply old-fashioned fundamentalist and strident hard-line Atheism *masked* as science.

The 14th-16th Century Vatican persecuting theorists for propounding helio-centrism, is now replaced by a hard-line Randomnist hierarchy in England (globally) undermining the careers of directional-universe theoreticians.

A zealous religious Inquisition is replaced by a zealous antireligious inquisition; Bogus Middle Ages Church doctrine is replaced by bogus 21st Century hard-line Random Universe doctrine.

In each case, too much power leading directly to ruinous and implacable hard-line doctrine - and from thence onto destruction of truth and lives.

Ultimately, the most powerful currency prevails in commerce, and the most powerful ideas/concepts prevail in the history of ideas. Thomas S. Kuhn discussed the fierce institutional resistance faced by paradigm challenges. See his 1962 classic, The Structure of Scientific Revolutions.

One can *argue* that my little Harvard degree is not in philosophy - or one can look at the overwhelming evidence behind the proposition - and 'listen to the music'.

I invite you to examine the hypothesis and expand your minds and your souls.

Sincerely,

David B.

MANHATTAN

see also formal inductive proof: **Inductive1000.com**

David.Birnbaum.NY@gmail.com

Religious, Spiritual or Secular?

Quest for Potential$^\infty$

So is Q4P Religious, Spiritual or Secular? The theorist crafted three different companion works to deal with these three classic possible different lenses. And he wishes to leave the question unanswered. Partly because he has no definitive answer, and partly because he feels that both *humanity's interest* and the *humanistic interest* lie in leaving that particular question unresolved.

Of course, the same individual, even the author, can look at the universe through all three lenses, even simultaneously...

our 'Smart Universe' driven by our hypothesized *natural force* (Q4P)

to order direct via Amazon click **SummaAmazon**

With special homage to timeless thinkers -

A.I. Kook
Pierre Teilhard de Chardin
Thomas Merton

We hitch a ride on the shoulders of giants,
so we can potentially scan the edge of the horizon
just a touch further out....

And, of course we salute our esteemed guide Guatama Buddha

- Birnbaum

Thank You

Thank you for graciously reviewing this presentation.

I hope I have laid out the argument cogently.

D.B.

[for the fuller treatment, see SummaMetaphysica.com, of course.]

David.Birnbaum.NY@gmail.com

Wrapping-up

https://www.summametaphysica.com/related-commentary/

Has the Entrenched Randomness Clique Strangled Global Debate?

Commentary

The Closing of the Scientific Mind

01.01.14 - 12:00 AM | David Gelernter

❝

Bullying Nagel.

The modern "mind fields" encompass artificial intelligence, cognitive psychology, and philosophy of mind. Researchers in these fields are profoundly split, and the chaos was on display in the ugliness occasioned by the publication of Thomas Nagel's *Mind & Cosmos* in 2012. Nagel is an eminent philosopher and professor at NYU. In *Mind & Cosmos*, he shows with terse, meticulous thoroughness why mainstream thought on the workings of the mind is intellectually bankrupt. He explains why Darwinian evolution is insufficient to explain the emergence of consciousness—the capacity to feel or experience the world. He then offers his own ideas on consciousness, which are speculative, incomplete, tentative, and provocative—in the tradition of science and philosophy.

Nagel was immediately set on and (symbolically) beaten to death by all the leading punks, bullies, and hangers-on of the philosophical underworld. Attacking Darwin is the sin against the Holy Ghost that pious scientists are taught never to forgive. Even worse, Nagel is an atheist unwilling to express sufficient hatred of religion to satisfy other atheists. There is nothing religious about Nagel's speculations; he believes that science has not come far enough to explain consciousness and that it must press on. He believes that Darwin is not sufficient.

The intelligentsia was so furious that it formed a lynch mob. In May 2013, *the Chronicle of Higher Education* [Washington, DC] ran a piece called "Where Thomas Nagel Went Wrong." One paragraph was notable:

> Whatever the validity of [Nagel's] stance, its timing was certainly bad. The war between New Atheists and believers has become savage, with Richard Dawkins writing sentences like, "I have described atonement, the central doctrine of Christianity, as vicious, sadomasochistic, and repellent. We should also dismiss it as barking mad...." In that climate, saying anything nice at all about religion is a tactical error.

It's the cowardice of the Chronicle's statement that is alarming—as if the only conceivable response to a mass attack by killer hyenas were to run away. Nagel was assailed; almost everyone else ran. 🙼

The Closing of the Scientific Mind.

That science should face crises in the early 21st century is inevitable. Power corrupts, and science today is the Catholic Church around the start of the 16th century: used to having its own way and dealing with heretics by excommunication, not argument.

Science is caught up, also, in the same educational breakdown that has brought so many other proud fields low. Science needs reasoned argument and constant skepticism and open-mindedness. But our leading universities have dedicated themselves to stamping them out—at least in all political areas. We routinely provide superb technical educations in science, mathematics, and technology to brilliant undergraduates and doctoral students. But if those same students have been taught since kindergarten that you are not permitted to question the doctrine of man-made global warming, or the line that men and women are interchangeable, or the multiculturalist idea that all cultures and nations are equally good (except for Western nations and cultures, which are worse), how will they ever become reasonable, skeptical scientists? They've been reared on the idea that questioning official doctrine is wrong, gauche, just unacceptable in polite society. (And if you are president of Harvard, it can get you fired.) 🙼

About the Author
David Gelernter is a professor of computer science at Yale. His book *Subjectivism: The Mind from Inside* will be published by Norton later this year.

A Cancer in Academe?

Current academe is heavily under the sway of a group of academics aligned with what is often referred to as the 'entrenched orthodoxy' schema. This schema's mantra is that the universe is barren and random; its advocates are often atheistic.

By admin on 7 February, 2014 7:51 am in Uncategorized / no comments

A January 2014 Commentary Magazine feature article The Closing of the Scientific Mind by David Gelernter, professor of computer science at Yale, takes the scientific and academic community to task on several inter-related fronts. One of the focuses of the piece is the 'totalitarian state' nature of current academe.
Current academe is heavily under the sway of a group of academics aligned with what is often referred to as the 'entrenched orthodoxy' schema. This schema's mantra is that the universe is barren and random; its advocates are often atheistic. The hybrid universe-view of this group is referred to as Randomness/atheistic. This academic group's geographic center-of-gravity is at seven leading colleges in southern England; the group refers to itself as the 'golden triangle' of universities; the iconic University of Cambridge plays a possibly disproportionate role in this matrix.
Academics from this Randomness/atheist group often informally act in-tandem. Additionally, segments in the media of the global atheist community at-large tend to act as an informal but aggressively proactive 'support group.'

As noted, the particular academic group believes that everything is random happenstance. In turn, they assert that mankind is inconsequential in the grander scheme of things, being but a cosmic accident of no significance and importance. To this group, mankind is but an insignificant speck in a cold, random and aimless universe. And as far as the billions of extraordinary galaxies each with billions of extraordinary stars and assorted planetary systems, well, just a random event you know. It all sort of just happened.

The Randomness/atheist group rejects any possibility of any transcending force or dynamic or design or spirituality or purpose in the universe. To them the universe is barren. If there is any common denominator to the universe, they would single out 'decay.' Standard bearer for atheism, noted chemistry author Peter Atkins asserts in his book Creation Revisited, "All change...arises from an underlying collapse into chaos...what may appear to us to be motive and purpose is in fact ultimately motiveless, purposeless decay." To the 'entrenched orthodoxy' many philosophical themes are taboo – including cosmic purpose, cosmic design, optimism regarding the cosmic future, or the importance of mankind.

Scientist David Gelernter criticizes the scientific academic community for becoming both pathologically 'politically correct' and militantly intolerant of 'dissent.' That is, faculty and students are encouraged to buy-into Randomness/atheism; anyone who dares challenge the dominant theory is often belittled and/or delegitimized by the academic hierarchy and its surrogates.

The Randomness/atheist crew learned from its model and former arch-enemy, the Medieval Church. Indeed, the Randomness/atheist crew does to intellectual challengers what the Medieval Church did to challengers of its own monopoly on 'truth': demonize, dehumanize and delegitimize. The Church rationalized its assorted crimes as in 'defense of our Lord Jesus Christ'; the British academic junta and its zealous supporters rationalize its own often nefarious gambits as in 'defense of science and truth.' The slogans are slightly different; however, the tactics of the Medieval Church and Randomness/atheist advocates are indeed the same. Both cloak their respective brutal power plays in the garments of nobler aims, whether 'God's truth' in the case of the Medieval Church, or alleged 'scientific truth' in the case of Randomness/atheism. Gelernter further writes "Power corrupts, [Randomness/atheistic] science today is the Catholic Church around the start of the 16th century: used to having its own way and dealing with heretics by excommunication, not argument." But in a Media Age, the British Randomness/atheist academic support group has brought defamation to an 'art form.' Intellectual challengers of Randomness/atheism are targeted by the hierarchy. Disinformation and pejorative quotes are planted in the media. Then this same disinformation and the related pejorative quotes and articles are used by more established academics and media to bury the reputation of the target. All in the name of 'objective reporting and discourse' of course. Any challenge to the hierarchy of Randomness/atheism is treated as High Treason by those who defend it; Gelernter cites the vicious tag-team relationship between the entrenched orthodoxy and The Chronicle of Higher Education in Washington DC. The online journal is the contemporary designated 'attack dog' deployed by the 'entrenched orthodoxy' of the academic establishment.

British libel laws are tough, so the British hierarchy uses the American-based and atheism-friendly The Chronicle of Higher Education as its 'hit man.' Hiding behind American 'freedom of the press' and with a penchant for no boundaries tabloid-style reporting, the establishment-connected online journal is not shy at playing rough and dirty with challengers of the entrenched Randomness/atheistic dogma. Standard journalistic integrity often finds itself an orphan in these confines.

Gelernter shows how the agenda-driven Chronicle goes ballistic when the Randomness/atheists are intellectually challenged. He cites the current case of NYU Professor of Philosophy Thomas Nagel. In 2012 Oxford University Press published Nagel's work Mind & Cosmos. The gut core thesis of the work is relatively simple: Contemporary evolutionary biology theory a.k.a. 'the entrenched orthodoxy' has been conceptually unable to handle the emergence of consciousness. Nagel thereupon immediately becomes the arch-enemy to be bullied and trashed by the 'lynch mob' (Gelernter's term) from the academic hierarchy working in tandem with The Chronicle. Galernter writes: "Nagel is an eminent philosopher and professor at NYU. In Mind & Cosmos, he shows with terse, meticulous thoroughness why mainstream thought [the 'entrenched orthodoxy'] on the workings of the mind is intellectually bankrupt. He explains why Darwinian evolution is insufficient to explain the emergence of consciousness—the capacity to feel or experience the world. He [Nagel] then offers his own ideas on consciousness, which are speculative, incomplete, tentative, and provocative—in the tradition of science and philosophy.

Nagel was immediately set on and (symbolically) beaten to death by all the leading punks, bullies, and hangers-on of the philosophical underworld. Attacking Darwin is the sin against the Holy Ghost that pious scientists are taught never to forgive. Even worse, Nagel is an atheist unwilling to express sufficient hatred for religion to satisfy other atheists."

Objectively the Nagel challenge was quite mild, and indeed published by Oxford University Press no less. However, even a scintilla of dissent is rabidly pounced-upon by The Chronicle and other members of the atheist support group of the Randomness/atheist academicians.

In the process of the hyper-aggressiveness of this support group, the major British universities of the Randomness/atheist academics become a party to the intellectually and morally tainted tactics. Ditto for the Royal Society Fellowship. The major and iconic British universities as well as the Royal Society have allowed themselves to become a party to the betrayal of the public trust at-large. They have all remained disingenuously silent while vicious gambits have been deployed against dissenting voices for over two decades.

In sycophancy with The Chronicle they cumulatively de facto suppress debate and undermine the reputations of intellectual challengers. The British academic hierarchy advocating Randomness/atheism has been a party to this stifling of debate for over two decades. Notwithstanding its fancy pedigree, it has single-handedly set back global debate and the global advance of knowledge.

The Fall of Randomness

subtext: the ramifications of the Randomness clique's abuse of power

The m.o.:
From the shadows, their 'leadership clique' has *rationalized* a pattern of
ongoing nefarious antics/gambits to destroy competing theorists.

unable to compete 'on the merits'
the clique deploys *academic thuggery -*
with *slander, defamation, and misinformation*
as consistently central to its messaging
- in targeting opposing theorists for destruction

The net result:
Institutionalizing the strangulation (by the Randomness clique) of global debate
as (somehow) *acceptable academic practice & norm*

extra-legal modus operandi
one cannot assert that their m.o. is a legal one
Is the closest descrition - 'racketeering & corrupt' ?

a few medieval ogres calling their shots
suppress all debate * crush all dissent * destroy all dissenters

actually a fundamentalist/hard-line/militant/nihilistic cult
masquerading as a scientific theory

radicalizing classic Atheism
- from (scientifically tenable) ideological opposition to classic Creationist God,
into (scientifically untenable) hard-line Atheism -
with strident opposition to any 'direction' whatsoever in the universe
as core doctrine.

In the mix,
Their stratagem conveniently aims to toxify competing theorists
(typically American),
and attempts to sideline these American theories (typically 'directional universe').

The 'cover':
slap-on-the-back jocularity and pompous self-righteous (misplaced) arrogance

The internal (delusional) mantra:
"We are Imperial" - and we alone - and unilaterally -

will decide what is acceptable academic discourse

Conflating an anti-religious ideology
- with academic teachings

As 90%+ of science academicians in England happen to conveniently be hard-line Atheists, many will merge a fundamentalist ideology (stridently anti-theist), with a (false) scientific hunch (an anti-directional universe); they will then advocate Randomness/Aimlessness - as (alleged) science.
The two themes: a strident fundamentalist ideology and a (false) hunch - will become *one and the same*: the (convoluted) 'science' of the Atheist British academics.

the putative 'side benefit':
Presumably the Randomness clique would get to divvy-up global academic influence -
with 'legacy' and sundry accolades *in-the-mix*....

the ancillary toxic gambits:
the 'gaming' of Google and Wikipedia

teaching the wrong course
The Randomness clique should not be teaching Cosmology;
they should be teaching a course which they actually truly understand:
"Fascism for Beginners" : An Introductory Course

does not actually qualify as science
should not really even be brought up in the Science Department courses;
sort of, a *wrong turn* in the history of science;
simply *not serious*

hijacked and mutated classic Atheism
mutated Atheism from: disbelievers in classic God >
rabid and millitant opponents of any 'direction' to the universe

Zombie DNA
we come, we destroy; darkness trumps light; despair trumps hope

We are the nihilist Randomness cultists

Three racketeering identity-masked ghouls on pinnacle British campuses
are allowed to decree verdicts of academic *Life or Death*
on cosmology/philosophy academics across America ???
- while Cambridge - Oxford - Imperial
hear no evil; see no evil ?
- while cutting-edge American theorists are conveniently undermined
and/or systematically destroyed?
- And while The Chronicle (DC-based) always 'happens' to deliver

the core (often virulently) negativity attack? - which can *conveniently and readily* be parlayed by the ghouls' acolytes into a high-profile destructive Guardian article and/or
Wikipedia piece to aid & abet the steady academic asphyxiation of the target theorist?

a (very) small secretive, psychologically twisted clique
- dictates (quack) 'science' to the world?

- by neutralizing/eliminating competing theorists via -
secretly commissioned *toxic articles;* bare-knuckled *academic blackmail;* and gaming Google/Wikipedia?

The *core Randomness hierarchy permanently* in hiding?

Three thuggish *from-the-shadows misfits...*

Self-appointed to play
judge-jury-executioner...

Sadistic cowards...

[NOTE. My family exited Berlin in 1938; we have seen these *fascist freaks* before...]

The collateral damage:
a 100+ year (at least as far back as 1900) freeze of scientific advance across multiple fields
a betrayal of the world's trust in British academe
the unhinging of England's venerable core academic integrity

*

But, as noted in the above Scroll Down, Randomness - as front & center - now falls on both key fronts: Cosmology and Evolution

*And, all the king's horses
and all the king's men*

*Couldn't put Humpty Dumpty
back together again*

"The world is not flat - and the universe is not random" - Birnbaum

see also SuperFormula1000.com

To the Reader

I have worked on this project since age ten (1960), 57 years ago, when I was a 4th grade student at (Modern Orthodox Jewish) Yeshiva Dov Revel of Forest Hills, Queens, NY.

About 1/2 of the parents had emigrated from Europe at some point post-1900, some tattooed with blue numbers on their forearms. Everyone was motivated. Dual-curriculum Dov Revel was the toughest school I ever attended, Harvard-included. Per the school's DNA, established science trumped theology. And, of course, we were exposed to challenge on all fronts.

On the science front, things were hopping in the '50s and '60s in Astronomy, in particular. As you recall, in Spring 1964 Bell Labs researchers in nearby NJ accidentally corroborated the Big Bang via cosmic microwave background radiation, and a new era was de facto ushered in. That vey same Spring 1964, I graduated eighth grade. My little Astronomy hobby morphed into my little Metaphysics hobby.

As you know, the first (volume of the Summa series) work came out 1988, 29 years ago.

I have studied the world and the theory from as many angles as I could during this entire 55+ year duration (1960 - now). The theory has been exhaustively vetted. At the 3+ day 2012 BARD conference, no vulnerability was discerned in Summa/Potentialism.

I am confident in the theory.

Please be wary of any academic group - however fancy - whose signature *m.o.* is the de-legitimization and defamation of competing theorists; whose single-minded stratagem is the relentless obfuscation or suppression of debate - at all costs.

This is my chosen modality to break the little stranglehold of that crypto-academic group.

May *truth* and *global advance* be the ultimate victors.

VERITAS.

Humbly submitted to my fellow voyagers on life's extraordinary journey.

Onward!

D. Birnbaum

NY

David.Birnbaum.NY@gmail.com

alert to the enemies of science masquerading as fancy academics:

Rumor has it
that a core (*con artist*) sub-group of
Darwinists and Random Universe theorists -
deploying toxicity from the shadows -
has almost perfected the art of *'character assassination'*
(of 'Directional Universe' theorists)

RICO

US RICO Act:
[Racketeeering Influenced and Corrupt Organization Act]

re: racketeering
via - serial, orchestrated, organized & concerted
attempted reputational rape gambits

USD $300,000 Reward

[$50,000- per imprisonment]

- for information leading to the arrest, (extradition), conviction and
  imprisonment of any culpable individuals - including any corrupted
  members of -

the contemporary extended Darwin clan (of Cambridge, England,
  London et al.)
  and trusts or agents thereof
  and/or

the (iconic) Cambridge University* - and its global 'ecosystem' -
   including any trustee, director, chancellor, hierarchy member, faculty,
   research assistant, alumni or patron
   and/or
including, but not limited to, Darwin College (founded 1964) on the
   Cambridge University campus -

   potentially found to be engaged-in illegally undermining the open
   dissemination of ideas of Directional Universe theorists globally
   via
   defamation, 'reputational rape', academic blackmailing or blackballing,
   and/or harassment, threats, and bullying
   including via
   corruptly gaming Wikipedia with corrupted information and spin - via
   'swarming' in the malevolent furtherance of the above

* many at powerful Cambridge U hold-up Darwin as their most illustrious
  alumnus - and 90% of British academe is heavily, if not zealously, invested-in
  related 'randomness' theories

New Paradigm Matrix Foundation
New York, NY
confidential reward channel: DBprivate@aol.com

Note from a Friend
to
University of Cambridge

Best not to allow a foothold on your campuses to those
who would strangle global debate

Respectfully do not allow academic thugs to *hide behind your skirts*

Best not to allow *enemies of science* to position yourselves as their *'enablers'*

"Scientia Imperii decus et tutamen"

How a Super-Select British Academic Elite
Betrayed England...and Science

Sci· ence ('sīəns) *noun* – 1. the intellectual and practical activity
encompassing the systematic study of the structure and behavior of
the physical and natural world through observation and experiment.

By admin on 17 March, 2014

Britain's academic elite has long been synonymous with science. A bastion
of academic excellence, the world has traditionally looked to the Brits
for guidance and leadership in scientific discovery. But select members
of British academe have steadily and insidiously been afflicted with an
intellectual stagnation that threatens the basis of scientific discovery as a
whole.

Science requires the open acceptance of competing theoretical exploration
and the rigors of intellectual discourse. Over the last couple decades,
select British players have parted paths with this taxing adherence to
scientific standards. Driven by ideology above science, this cohort has
turned its back on innovation and thought in favor of an intellectual
orthodoxy that seeks to silence, instead of encourage, progress. A certain

pinnacle British university has slowly slipped under the rulership of a small, but extremely vocal, atheistic (and nihilistic) community.

Atheism, on the surface, would not seem an enemy of science. Far from it, atheism has traditionally been viewed as the purest distillate of scientific inquiry. However, in the realm of cosmology, atheism has proven more deterrent than champion of scientific inquiry and thought. The root of the problem is Randomness.

A favorite theory amongst atheists, Randomness is a cosmological theory based on the idea that the universe is essentially entropic – chaotic and tending naturally towards disorder and disintegration. Atheists are firmly in support of Randomness primarily for its inherent hostility towards teleology. Teleology describes a universe of creation and increasing complexity, one that moves with an inherent will or purpose towards an end goal.

Teleology wouldn't sound relevant to atheism, but it very much is. At issue is that teleology opens the door for the possibility of divinity – the existence of God. To be clear, teleology does not predict the existence of God, it only allows for the possibility. Such has been the reflexive response of atheist academia though, that the mere possibility of just *room* for the divine has been enough to engender vicious attacks from the atheist community.

Unfortunately, such attacks have necessitated academics to set aside their principles and classic *modus* of scientific inquiry. As a bastion of the orthodox scientific community, a certain pinnacle British university has committed the scientific sin of intellectual suppression in the name of atheism. By far the saddest irony though is that this pinnacle British university has had to embrace the worst tactics that are associated with fundamentalist religious orthodoxy. Like the Catholic church of previous centuries, this certain pinnacle British university has *de facto* been a party to assaults on the character of those who have dared to challenge atheist scientific theory, academically attempting to burn them at the stake for their scientific heresy. And like the church before them, they've tried to contain the progress of scientific knowledge through intimidation, fear and ignorance.

That this certain pinnacle British university has betrayed itself as an institute of higher learning is obvious. But it has done far worse. It has betrayed England as well – a country long synonymous with science and progress. Most sadly though, it has betrayed global scientific advance as a whole.

MORPHED COSMIC ORDER

Section Q

MORPHED COSMIC ORDER

Our universe inexorably strives after its purpose:

POTENTIALISM THEORY

to maximize & optimize its Potential

*"Potentialism Theory, at the forefront of
21st century theories of cosmology,
is an iconic paradigm challenge"*

POTENTIALISM THEORY

- the Epoch Times 6/4/14

"an intellectual odyssey"

POTENTIALISM THEORY

- NY Jewish Review

MORPHED COSMIC ORDER

JUBILEE NEWSPAPER

Home | Daily News | Sports | Business | Politics |

Big Brother?
The Curious Case of Randomness Theory

Most British academics, particularly in the atheist community, will cite Randomness Theory as the model to describe cosmic order. According to the theory, the universe is nothing more than a fluke; subsequent life and humanity are random happenstance; all is random chance and chaotic. Randomness, a theory in academe, dovetails with Atheism, an ideological movement, as both posit the absence of any order or design to the universe. Thus the global lay atheistic community has apparently adopted Randomness and provides aggressive support for it in media in which they have leverage. As bizarre as this concept may be, Randomness is considered the only acceptable theory by the British academic orthodoxy. With control over many academic journals and leverage over select media, a small but focused British atheist academic group has managed to entrench Randomness as the prevailing orthodoxy.

To be sure, this *group-think* has its detractors. Often derided as the "Emperor's Clothing", Randomness has been ridiculed as more ideologically than scientifically motivated. Its primary purpose is to remove any semblance of 'design' from universal theory. Mixing 'science' with 'religion' is a potentially dangerous and volatile mix. Highly-placed British academics have not only allowed this 'mix' to be institutionalized, they turn a blind eye to the egregious actions of their ideological 'support group', global Atheism.

To further this end of advancing Randomness, the entrenched orthodoxy has an ongoing structure in-place to destroy both any challenging theories as well as their presenters. In what can be seen as nothing less than actual character assassination, the British academic establishment has viciously attacked dissenters through concerted, ad hominem attacks. A tiny minority of rabid academics have effectively held the intellectual community hostage - to prevent innovation in cosmic theory. By artificially burnishing Randomness Theory's credentials as an unassailable truth they have effectively stymied the advance of knowledge. Yet, their very tactics remove the most important tests of scientific theory – integrity and the ability to stand up to challenge and debate.

Typically, targets of the atheist group are first crucified in The Chronicle of Higher Education; then the Chronicle article is heavily floated as gospel truth and linked by atheist media globally; finally, the atheist network *ad nauseum* quotes defamatory pieces circulated by its own fellow members trashing the target. The initial result is a cascade of delegitimization globally focused on a single target. The end result is to prop-up Randomness by undermining any intellectual challenge. This cynical game has been countenanced by disingenuous senior British academics for over two decades, as they self-ward each other sundry awards and prizes. This ultimate 'closed club' has no choice but to self-congratulate fellow members in-on-the-game.

With no little irony, atheism currently stands where the Church once did. Through multiple mechanisms, such as controlling journals and academic media, the 21st century Church of Atheism has waged war on intellectual freedom and progress. Take, for example, Intelligent Design. Intelligent Design was introduced with significant components qualifying as legitimate theory. It had strong intellectual backing from segments of the academic community; right or wrong it had credible philosophical structure.
The atheist academic community, far from viewing it as legitimate, engaged in an all-out war on Intelligent Design. Instead of engaging in meaningful debate against the theory, the academic orthodoxy ridiculed and delegitimized both the theory and any proponents willing to support it. The entry-point' argument of the Intelligent Design group is tat 'design' seems apparent in the universe and in nature. Through various morally dubious gambits, the zealot Randomness-atheist group has managed to demonize this qute legitimate intellectual position.

While fostering lively debate is a hallmark of proper academics, what the British academic hierarchy has condoned if not instigated is more closely associated with the gambits of defamation, libel and character assassination. This should hardly be shocking though. 1918 Nobel Prize winner in Physics winner Max Planck (arguably the father of modern quantum physics) famously noted in his autobiography *Wis-senschaftliche Selbstbiographie. Mit einem Bildnis und der von Max von Laue gehaltenen Traueransprache* (Leipzig 1948): "A new scientific truth does not triumph by convincing its opponents and making them see the light, but rather because its opponents eventually die, and a new generation grows up that is familiar with it." Sadly, this may mean that the only way to banish the old superstitions of Randomness are for those too blind to lexit the stage, to fade into history.

A central tenrt of Randomness is "decay". Randomness Theory states that everything in the universe has a natural tendency to disintegrate and decline. Never mind that the universe's first moments of creation contradict this supposition. Never mind that the Law of Conservation of Mass states nothing can be destroyed. Never mind that the changing nature of the universe actually gave rise to complex, sentient life. Never mind that the advocates of decay go ballistic when one aks them *the source* of that which is decaying. All these obvious weak points are off-limits to challengers of Randomness Theory. To question the jih proests of Randomness-atheism is to flirt with academic ruin; the atheist pinnacle predators who defend Randomness will come after you, en masse.

One doesn't have to look far to find examples of these attacks.

In April 2012, Bard College hosted a three-day international academic conference show-casing private scholar David Birnbaum's iconic Summa Metaphysica philosophy treatise. In his work, Birnbaum proposes his dynamic and scientifically-based Infinite Potential Theory – possibly the most elegant metaphysics ever presented. Global academic acceptance of Summa notwithstanding, the British Randomness-atheist academics organized what can only be described as a "hit squad" against anyone Summa-related. In May of 2013, the Randomness junta retaliated in academic media in a mass, ad hominem attack on both Birnbaum and Bard (and any academic willing to stand by Birnbaum) – threatening the names and careers of anyone or anything that was associated with Infinite Potential Theory. What was left unspoken was how Birnbaum's Theory of Potential puts sketchy and intellectually vacuous Randomness Theory to shame. The cavalier British academic atheists seem to confuse power with truth.

The main attack against yeshiva-educated and Harvard-educated

Birnbaum is that he is an 'outsider' to the academic establishment. Iconic philosophy 'outsiders' 17th century Spinoza and 20th century Teilhard de Chardin, to name just two, might be bemused by the apparently panic-filled Randomness-atheistic establishment hell-bent on undermining paradigm challenger Birnbaum. The Randomness attack-dogs conveniently fail to note the dozen+ colleges globally using this particular 'outsider's's philosophical treatise as a course text. Note that notwithstanding the intense academic scrutiny, no flaw or vulnerability has been found or discerned over the 26-year span that Birnbaum's 3-volume treatise has been released.

Likewise, American philosopher Thomas Nagel challenged Randomness in his 2012 book Mind & Cosmos (Oxford Press). Ironically, Nagel himself is an atheist, but not part of the ruling junta. However, Nagel's belief that a universal model of purpose was missing from the Randomness model was enough to enrage the entrenched academic orthodoxy and set off a string of vicious personal attacks on him. Meanwhile the Randomness-atheist hierarchy scratches each other's backs and then mutually bestows awards upon one another 'for scientific advance', of course. Cute.

So vitriolic and unabashed have these gratuitous and baseless atheist attacks become, that some brave academics are speaking up to protest the damage done to the advancement of knowledge itself. In January of 2013, Yale Professor David Galernter, struck back at the atheist academic establishment with an article titled The Closing of the Scientific Mind. Enraged by the lasting damage caused by the reactionary browbeating of intellectual discovery, Galernter lashed-out at these 'lynch-mob' crypto-academics for what he called 'locker-room braggadocio' deployed to belittle legitimate intellectual challenge. Galernter maintains that it is the intimidation of science and the vicious tactics of those defending Randomness, that is causing science to suffer and stagnate.

This all begs the question: How does this gang have any legitimacy at all? Have they not betrayed the sacred trust accorded to academia – to search out truth? Have they not thoroughly abused their power at the helm of academe? Has this so-elite group of fancy academic from fancy British universities not shown itself to be both morally and intellectually bankrupt? Moreover, do the proponents of Randomness actually have anything of substance to say? Or his the whole production of

Randomness Theory just a 'house of cards' artificially propped-up on media life-support by a small clique of academics zealouslu protecting their little academic power turf and clubby Church (of Atheism)? Is Randomness even a theory – or more an absence of a theory? If it is indeed a theory, why do its defenders refuse to give any breathing space for opposition? Why do they – in knee-jerk fashion - choose to rabidly attack both message and messenger with such morally reprehensible tactics?

Are they are just 'hollow men with hollow theories?' Just how long do they expect to keep this dubious charade going? More importantly, when their ongoing nefariousness is uncovered, how much greater will the public revulsion when the full extent of their decades-long gangster-like gambits surfaces? Perhaps Randmoness-atheist academics should actually consider being scientists first, and zealous, extremist loyalists of the Church of Atheism second.

As for the contemporary pioneers of modern philosophy and cosmology viciously attacked by the Randomness junta and their lackeys, kudos to them for staying steadfast and unbowed -- as well as for their intellectual daring and conceptual brilliance. Consider these words from an address on the 25th Anniversary of the Kaiser Wilhelm Society (January 1936): "New scientific ideas never spring from a communal body, however organized, but rather from the head of an individually inspired researcher who struggles with his problems in lonely thought and unites all his thought on one single point which is his whole world for the moment. "In that vein, the Birnbams and Nagels of today are the inheritors of science, the Newtons, Plancks and Galileos of the new millennia.

Summa Metaphysica's intro presciently quotes 20th century European philosopher-poet Lanza del Vasto "All revolutions take time to settle in." Intellectual mavericks and allies Birnbaum and Nagel have come to symbolize resistance to the terror-tactics of a disingenuous reactionary group operating 'from the shadows' and committed only to their personal power and ideological zealotry. Although vastly outgunned, both intellectual revolutionaries Birnbaum and Nagel remain steadfast and confident that they will prevail, perhaps secure in 19th Century French writer Victor Hugo's adage "Nothing is more powerful than an idea whose time has come".

WHO KNEW?

note the terrifying *alternate title*
'PRESERVATION OF......
of Darwin's key work

ON

THE ORIGIN OF SPECIES

BY MEANS OF NATURAL SELECTION,

OR THE

PRESERVATION OF FAVOURED RACES IN THE STRUGGLE
FOR LIFE.

By CHARLES DARWIN, M.A.,

FELLOW OF THE ROYAL, GEOLOGICAL, LINNÆAN, ETC., SOCIETIES;
AUTHOR OF 'JOURNAL OF RESEARCHES DURING H. M. S. BEAGLE'S VOYAGE
ROUND THE WORLD.'

LONDON:

JOHN MURRAY, ALBEMARLE STREET.

1859.

Some posit that the iconic Darwin work served as the
quack-science underpinning for the Third Reich's nefarious and murderous eu-
genics undertakings.

Note the 'heavily-loaded' terminology (alternate title) -
"PRESERVATION OF FAVOURED RACES IN THE STRUGGLE FOR LIFE".

And note the ominous
resonance with the German Mein Kampf (My Struggle),
Hitler's key work 66 years later.

The time arc from the Liberation of Auschwitz to now is 75 years to the day (Jan 27, 2020); the toxicity emanating from the quack-cohort bowels of Britain is more intense than ever.

So, now we have an additional suspect group (aside from pathological /obsessive British nationalists rooting for hometown favorite Darwin) - for the virulence and magnitude of the vicious anonymous attacks and planted defamations - on theorists not playing ball with Darwinism.

BRITISH BLOOD SPORT

Darwinism - and somewhat related 'Random Universe'
- as theories may be *'dead man walking'*;
but that does not stop Wikipedia editors belonging to Darwin clubs -
of a certain pinnacle British university
from criminally gaming Wikipedia - via Brit *Wiki-editor-swarming*
- to smear and defame - and endeavoring to invalidate & sideline -
directional universe theorists.

Swarm, Game & Defame is our name.

Trash & Academically Blackmail
any academic body
giving a major platform to a Directional Universe Theorist

We - the Brits - have learned well
from our ancient adversary - the medieval Catholic Church

"Stifle global debate
Stymie the global advance of knowledge
Smear any Directional Universe Theorists
God Save the Queen
Darwinism uber alles"

All glory is fleeting

Randomness/Aimlessness (as the key 'cosmic catalyst') is *'done'* (debunked).[1] .

The Darwinism version of Evolution is *'done'* (debunked).[2] .

The anti-scientific *'infinite random universes'* formulation is *'done' (debunked).*[3]

The 100+ year *dark ages* brought to you courtesy of the British randomnist cabal will now start to steadily collapse of its own *intellectual and moral bankruptcy.*

*

all elucidated above in RewindSumma.com:

*1 Quest for Potential is the prime catalyst

*2 Fusion Evolution trumps Darwinism / See Evolution1000.com

*3 Any/all universes need-be Potential-driven and directional

The Stealth Mob

Why does the 'British academic mob'
[the inter-related
SELF SELECTING -
British jingoists - Darwinists - Randomnists - Hard Line Atheists]
attack from the shadows?

Because it does not *have the goods* to attack on the merits.

The mob's inter-related modalities are -
    defamation, bullying, academic blackmail, character assassination
        - *and the like*

A corrupt British cohort

And what do the Brits gain?

The preponderance of the British hi-achiever metaphysics / physics/
cosmology players are vested in Randomness Theory;
meaning, they all vector towards a Non-Directional Universe theme.

THUS, any Directional Universe theory or theorist - *is the enemy.*

But, the 'mob' is holding a (fatally) weak intellectual hand with its
Random (non-directional) Universe *British Kool Aid.***

THUS, to preserve its power/glory/status/awards/prerogatives/legacy/
sway
                it resorts to trashing/invalidating its opponents
                        - from the shadows

            The intent is to suppress/quash free debate -
                as free debate would be perilous

From their perspective, best to enjoy a monopoly

    until, at least the challenger is sufficiently disingenuously publicly
    debased / invalidated / undermined / distorted / de-legitimized
            - so as to have *de minimus credibility*

>>>

At all costs, the mob does not want a debate - *on the merits*

The mob has, indeed, thwarted the advance of global debate and knowledge for well-over a century.

Quite a notorious - and noxious hypocritical feat.

As far as the Brits - and their fancy shills at Cambridge U *et al* are concerned
  THEY WIN - until they are exposed -
    and then they LOSE

The nation of Newton -
  has now premiered an academic cohort of
    neo-criminals

It is, pathetically, the 'swan song' of a once-great empire.

Sold their souls - and *sold-out* the students of the world

    How the Mighty Have Fallen

    *

* Darwin is the stellar grad of Cambridge U - and a superstar in the British pantheon, in particular.

** Yes / Much that goes on in the universe is random, but randomness does not *define the universe*; the universe is directional - Potential-driven at its core. See Direction1000. com - or a random section of 4-volume Summa Metaphysica, as a start.

Onward!

POTENTIALISM THEORY 1988

Q4P$^\infty$

Q4P$^\infty$ → C+ → E+

The Contemporary Darwin Family 'Bogeyman'
- *in the equation*

focused Time Line

1831   Charles Darwin graduates University of Cambridge (aka Cambridge U); he will later become its most celebrated grad

1859   Charles Darwin publishes *On the Origin of Species*

1960s   The 1960s decade marks five generations later / Darwin family time-line

1964   Darwin College (Cambridge, England) founded as a constituent college of Cambridge U
        # exclusively for Graduate Students
        # location treated as the same extended Cambridge U campus;
        # land furnished-by Darwin Family

2001   Wikipedia founded

2012   Bard College / Upstate NY / April 16-19 Conference on Metaphysics / Summa Metaphysica

2012   multi-year Global smear campaign launched v. Summa / we believe orchestrated by self-selecting actors from inter-related British cohorts: Darwin clubs / Randomness / Hard-Line Atheists / British jingoists - with center-of-gravity of the smear campaign we believe-to-be Cambridge U - including global alumni

2013   David Birnbaum / Wikipedia page / launched & defaced by toxic-swarm-attacks by British Wiki editors using pseudonyms & cloaked emails - but British origin clear; Wikipedia removes the page after multiple swarm-attacks

2013-   100+ articles appear re: Summa
2016   (see Summa-Supplement.com)
        99% overwhelmingly-positive; 1% snarky

2021   attempted-smear campaign by British-mob continues, but on a much lower scale

*** reward funds remain-in-place ***

Wikipedia and the Mob

For sure, by now Wikipedia knows that the Brit-mob has single-handedly destroyed its global credibility.

So, why has Wiki not moved against them?

'*The mob*' has subverted both *global debate* and Wikipedia's *credibility* ongoing.

All that Wikipedia has built-up since its launch (2001), '*the mob*' has *put-at-risk*.

The culprits are readily identifiable by Wikipedia.

MORPHED COSMIC ORDER

Potentialism-Summa

POTENTIALISM THEORY

unified / fully-integrated / holistic / 'everywhere' / flawless

---

To The Royal Society (London)

I invite you
to join us
in an exploration
of the Cosmic Code -
and of the Cosmic Order

Rumor has it
that you are a talented lot

Don't look back

THE OLD ORDER PASSETH

History beckons

- Birnbaum

David.Birnbaum.NY@gmail.com

Interesting

The Birnbaum Super-Formula (see Super-Formula1000.com) was promulgated explicitly in-depth back in 2005 via Summa II (Summa-2. com). See section Directional Universe.

Ever since the April 2012 Bard Conference (see Conference1000.com), the Randomness cult (centered in England) has vainly been grasping to find some flaw - any flaw, however miniscule - in Potentialism Theory (see Summa1000.com). The *Brit-Mob* has vainly grasped to find even one exception - even one small factoid in contradiction - to the Super-Formula - over the span of the 14 billion years of known cosmic history.

Then, to the chagrin of the Randomnists, 100+ favorable articles were published in 40+ journals on Potentialism / Summa Theory - building-out nuanced and typically (quite) positive commentary. See Summa-supplement.com.

The Super-Formula was then *front & center* highlighted in the Huffington Post major piece *David Birnbaum Cracks the Cosmic Code* June 10, 2015. See HuffPost1000.com.

The formula was then featured as a full-page ad on the back cover of *Scientific American* - Sept 2017 issue. See TheoryAd1000.com.

Alas, after all the frenetic mind-bending grasping, apparently no flaw or exception has been discerned - on either the macro or micro level - in the theory or its salient, the Super-Formula.

Not one.

Looping-back...

In 1988 Summa I (in-circulation 25,000+ copies - aside from online SummaMetaphysica.com 1988-present) introduced the rudimentary proposition of Quest for Potential.

Princeton's iconic John Wheeler's *It from bit* would be introduced by him in 1990 (two years after Summa I). MIT maverick Seth Lloyd's

Programming the Universe was published in 2006. For context, eighteen years after Summa I and one year after Summa II.

In the meanwhile, since 1988 (the publication date of Summa I) Randomness 'Theory' and its fellow traveler Darwinism Theory - have (unrelated to Summa) independently both taken innumerable significant *game-ending (meaning, existential)* intellectual/scientific *'torpedo hits'* - from across the global academic spectrum. [See YouTube....keyword phrases: Fine Tuned Universe..... Problems and Issues with Darwinism.]

Thus, my no-issue - and apparently No-Flaw Potentialism Theory - would seem to trump *fatally-flawed* (across multiple fronts) Randomness Theory [*aka* Theory of No Theory Randomness].

See TTOE1000.com - [Potentialsm:] The True Theory of Everything.

We shall see.

All so Interesting. ;)

'Beginner's Luck' for sure...

And, all-of-the above, with *'The Brit Mob'* - *via* its sundry sordid racketeering gambits - *in heat* to undermine the new theory (Potentialism).

And, as speculated by the 1960s David B,
the solution was, indeed,
hiding in plain sight
all-along.

From all angles, after 33+ years of
aggressive scrutiny and vetting since 1988,
the theory *is, so-far, bulletproof;*
and does not seem to have a serious challenger.

[This must be only rumor / for sure - Birnbaum]

Weaponize

[the basic m.o. of the Darwinist crew]

Weaponize -
　　the iconic British scientific journals
　　　　to sideline *directional universe* theorists

Weaponize -
　　the many University of Cambridge***
　　Research Associates
　　　　who are also Wiki editors
　　　　　　to then undermine the Wiki pages
　　　　　　　　of *directional universe* theorists

Weaponize -
　　Wikipedia from another direction, as well
　　a) unilaterally set up a Wikipedia page
　　re: the young *directional universe* theorist
　　b) swarm-attack the page to negatively brand the theorist, hopefully making
　　him radioactive forevermore
　　c) parry any positivity which objective observers attempt to place on the
　　WIKI page
　　d) leave the young theorist
　　　- in shock, disheartened and 'gasping for air'

　　>>> Essentially, to *kill the baby in the cradle*

　　- and, with a quick kill, optimally end forever - the particular threat to
　　Darwinian Theory's hegemony

Weaponize -
　　the same Research Associates
　　　　to harass the testimonial writers (globally)
　　　　　　of *directional universe* theorists
　　　　- and to browbeat, bully & compromise
　　　　　　the Conference organizers & Speakers
　　　　　　　　of a *directional universe* theorist Conference

Weaponize -
    the ecosystem - including global alumni - of University of Cambridge -
        to reward other Univ of Cambridge ecosystem members who *play ball*
            - and to punish any theorists globally who do not

Weaponize -
    key British journals
        to provide snarky, negative, and convoluted images
            of the *directional universe* theorist

Weaponize -
    sundry non-British media platforms
        (via the Univ of Cambridge global ecosystem)
            in which to so-innocently drop
                defamatory misinformation, distortions, and slander
                    re: the *directional universe* theorist
                        - which British journals can then safely reference
                        - and pile-on
                            [And, of course, this way, the British journals
                                themselves are disingenuously essentially shielded
                                    from tough British slander laws]

Weaponize -
    a portion of the fortune and trusts
    of a certain iconic British *landed gentry* clan
        - to fund, as appropriate - and *grease-the-wheels*
        of the nefariousness noted above

All in all,
a *full court press*
of toxicity
and, in a word, *racketeering*

***

alma mater of Charles Darwin
and
home of Darwin College

The alternate title for the above panel is -

"How to Betray the World"

*

end of

Summa Metaphysica IV
Quantum Man:
Morphed Cosmic Order

*

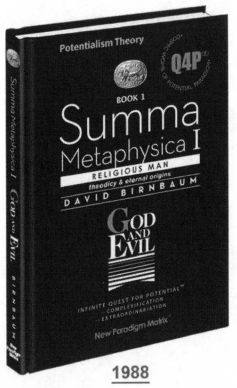

1988

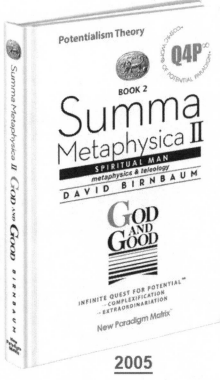

2005

2014

2020

MORPHED COSMIC ORDER

I HAVE RESPECTFULLY LAID-OUT THE CASE FOR POTENTIALISM THEORY
AS THE WORKING HYPOTHESIS FOR THE COSMIC ORDER

DAVID BIRNBAUM
NY
SUMMA METAPHYSICA IV

Miscellaneous

David Birnbaum

books by
BIRNBAUM

Metaphysics

www.SummaMetaphysica.com

see also
www.AmazonX1000.com

Summa I

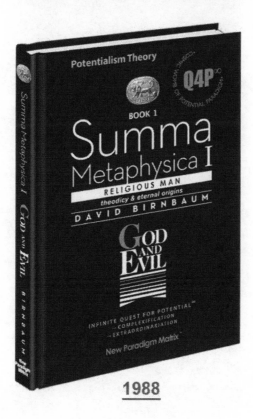

1988

Summa Metaphysica I:
Religious Man:
God and Evil
focus: *theodicy & eternal origins*

www.Summa-1.com

Summa II

2005

Summa Metaphysica II:
Spiritual Man:
God and Good
focus: *metaphysics & teleology*

www.Summa-2.com

Summa III

2014

Summa Metaphysica III:
Secular Man:
The Transcendent Dynamic
focus: *cosmology & evolution*

www.Summa-3 .com

Summa IV

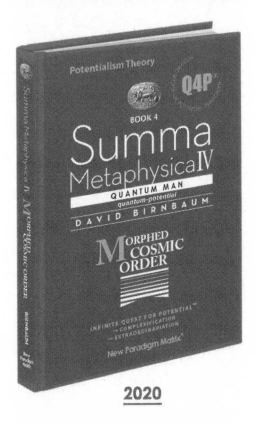

2020

Summa Metaphysica IV:
Quantum Man:
Morphed Cosmic Order
focus: *quantum-potential*

www.Summa-4.com

Summa Supplement

2016

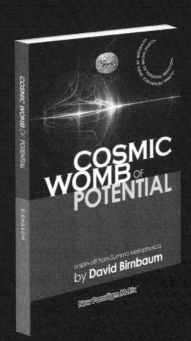

COSMIC WOMB OF POTENTIAL

COSMIC WOMB OF POTENTIAL

a spin-off from Summa Metaphysica
by David Birnbaum

New Paradigm Matrix

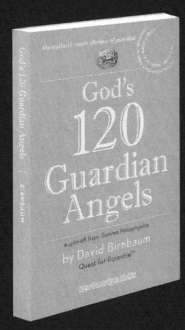

God's 120 Guardian Angels

the mythic of cosmic phalanx of potential

God's 120 Guardian Angels

a spin-off from Summa Metaphysica
by David Birnbaum
Quest for Potential

New Paradigm Matrix

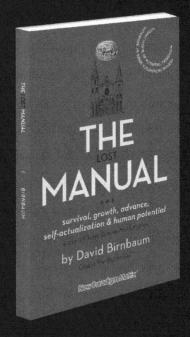

THE LOST MANUAL

THE LOST MANUAL

survival, growth, advance,
self-actualization & human potential

a spin-off from Summa Metaphysica
by David Birnbaum
Quest for Potential

New Paradigm Matrix

www.SummaSpinoffs.com

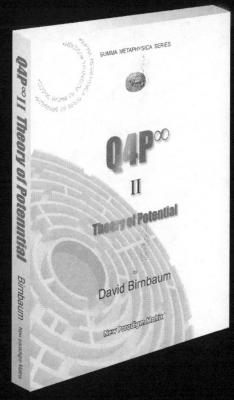

an artistic/graphic representation

www.TheoryGraphics1000.com

Metaphysics

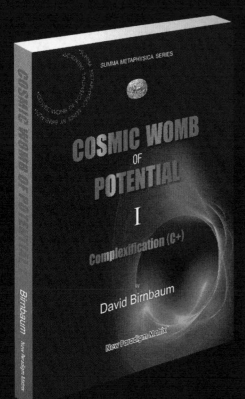

an artistic/graphic representation

www.TheoryGraphics1000.com

an artistic/graphic representation

www.TheoryGraphics1000.com

Metaphysics

an artistic/graphic representation

www.TheoryGraphics1000.com

21st CENTURY PUBLISHING

NPM1000@yahoo.com

www.NewParadigmMatrix.com

"A Major Work in the Philosophy of Religion"*

"...there is no comparable volume offering such a comprehensive, authoritative and intelligible discussion of the problem...a remarkable effort to offer a fresh approach..."
    Paul Mendez–Flohr
    Professor of Philosophy, Hebrew University,
    Jerusalem Editor, *Contemporary Jewish Religious Thought*

"...an original, and, in this reader's opinion, a very promising point of view...the author gathers a philosophically coherent and, in the end, highly modern insight... a unified metaphysics..."
    Louis Dupré
    Professor of Religious Studies, Yale University

"...a major work in the Philosophy of Religion... a masterful achievement...a novel and satisfying approach... a major intellectual achievement."
    *Canon William Johnson
    Professor of Philosophy, Brandeis University

"...a major contribution to the Jewish conversations through the ages, on theodicy, and the problem of evil generally."
Dr. Norman Lamm
President, Yeshiva University

"...a framework for a renewed exploration into the most agonizing aspects of the meaning of religious belief... It is an impressive attempt to focus intellectually on the Holocaust without diminishing the primal outcry of pain."
Rabbi Nachum Rabinovitch
Rosh Yeshiva Birkat Moshe, Israel,
Former Dean, Jews College, London

"David Birnbaum brings the rich resources of the Jewish tradition to bear on the universal problem of theodicy. The result is a new synthesis... I can certainly recommend it as a fascinating contribution to the philosophy of religion which merits the attention of Christians and Jews alike."
John J. Collins
Professor of Theology, University of Notre Dame
Editor, *Journal of Biblical Literature*

cont'd

[continued]

"*God and Evil* represents a bold attempt to formulate an ingenious theory, which, drawing upon creative reinterpretations of classical Jewish doctrine, places the Free Will Defense within a broader metaphysical framework..."
  Rabbi Walter S. Wurzburger
  Professor of Philosophy, Yeshiva University
  Editor, *Tradition*

"All who read this book will find much instruction, insight, and material for reflection...I find the overall thesis of the book touching and inspiring..."
  Rabbi Irving Greenberg
  President, The National Jewish Center for Learning and Scholarship (CLAL)

"A major work...a great intellectual and spiritual effort"
  Joseph Dan
  Professor of Kabbalah, Hebrew University

***

"the best book in print on the subject."
−HERITAGE JOURNAL

"Author and scholar David Birnbaum wrestles with the age−old problem of the existence of evil... a compelling, stimulating and creative contribution..."
−JUDAICA BOOK NEWS

"Birnbaum's God and Evil is an extremely significant volume which grapples forthrightly and originally with the problem... well−organized... clearly written... persuasive... Birnbaum comes as close as possible to solving the awesome dilemma of evil in a world created by a just God."
−JEWISH WORLD

"Birnbaum wrestles with the problem of evil from a Jewish perspective, but provides fresh insights for Christians as well. This is a good book, written in faith, and with honesty and passion..."
−THEOLOGICAL STUDIES
Georgetown University

"Wiesel and Birnbaum share a deep respect for, and loyalty to, their ancestral faith. Yet the contrast between their approaches is ultimately perhaps as instructive as the approaches themselves. Birnbaum's approach is essentially that of the intellectual, philosopher, and theologian..."
−CANADIAN CATHOLIC REVIEW

"a bold and highly original synthesis...audacious yet sensitive, traditional and yet highly innovative...yet within the parameters of an authentically Jewish halakhic point of view...an intellectual odyssey"
−JEWISH REVIEW

BARD COLLEGE

A PLACE TO THINK

THREE+ DAY
INTERNATIONAL ACADEMIC CONFERENCE

SCIENCE & RELIGION

with a focus on
Summa Metaphysica
by David Birnbaum

Monday through Thursday
April 16-19, 2012
Annandale-on-Hudson, NY

www.Conference1000.com

David Birnbaum's 'Quest for Potential' hypothesis

International Academic Conference

Science and Religion:

A Role for Metaphysics?

Reflections flowing

from David Birnbaum's *Summa Metaphysica*

"Works by David Birnbaum...
suggest that Metaphysics
may emerge as a critical field once again." *

- from Official Program Invitation & Introduction**

BARD College Conference, April 16-19, 2012

- Dr. Bruce Chilton, co-Chairman

- Dr. Gary Hagberg, co-Chairman

AT BARD
APRIL 2012

* [Meaning, after 300 year hiatus post-Spinoza]

** Conference1000.com

"MASTERPIECE"

- **AJHS**
  Heritage Journal
  New York

- **Nahum N. Glatzer**
  Boston University

- **Dr. Sanford Drob**
  Founder, NY Jewish Review

- **Professor William Johnson**
  Brandeis University

- **Rabbi Benjamin Blech**
  Yeshiva University

- **Professor Masako Nakagawa**
  Villanova University

Prospects For Mideast Peace?
Pages 4, 5

Sholem Aleichem: A Jewish Mark Twain
Page 13

LONG ISLAND
JewishWorld

Vol. 38# 11 March 20-26, 2009 • 24 Adar - Nisam 5769   One Dollar Two Dollars Outside of Metropolitan N.Y.C.

'Cracking the Cosmic Code'

In *God and Good,* the second in his *Summa Metaphysica* series, David Birnbaum tackles life's 'Big Questions'

Marvin Tokayer's interview begins on page 8

'God's 120 Guardian Angels,' by Sandford Drob page 8

A philosophical 'gamble,' by Daniel N. Khalil page 9

(Left): David Birnbaum in his Manhattan office with his two - volume set. The newly published God and Good (left, white cover) and God and Evil (right, black cover), published in 1988. (Right): Birnbaum as a young graduate student studying finance at Harvard in 1974 (right), a young Yitzchak Rabin, a visiting guest speaker

New Paradigm Matrix™

MANHATTAN

Phone: 212 - 695 - 6888   Fax: 212 - 643 - 1044

available on Amazon / go to www.SummaOptions.org

Onward!

Thank You
for your consideration of this
fully-integrated
metaphysics/philosophy/cosmology/teleology
hypothesis

*

Per Thomax Kuhn (1962),
scientific revolutions are hard-fought

*

I assure you that I am quite humbled
by the gravitas - and stakes -
of this entire undertaking

*

David Birnbaum
New York

1-on-1   David Birnbaum - Deepak Chopra

OCT 2018

Chopra1000.com

Q4P theory

BIRNBAUM WORKS

Summa Metaphysica I GOD AND EVIL BIRNBAUM — New Paradigm Matrix — 1988

Summa Metaphysica II GOD AND GOOD BIRNBAUM — New Paradigm Matrix — 2005

Summa Metaphysica III THE TRANSCENDENT DYNAMIC BIRNBAUM — New Paradigm Matrix — 2014

Summa Metaphysica IV MORPHED COSMICORDER BIRNBAUM — New Paradigm Matrix — 2020

Summa Metaphysica ARTICLES ON SUMMA BIRNBAUM — New Paradigm Matrix — online only

THE CRUCIFIXION Book 1 — New Paradigm Matrix — 2009

THE CRUCIFIXION Book 2 BIRNBAUM — New Paradigm Matrix — 2009

VOLUME I JEWS, CHURCH & CIVILIZATION I BIRNBAUM — New Paradigm Matrix — 2010

VOLUME II JEWS, CHURCH & CIVILIZATION II BIRNBAUM — New Paradigm Matrix — 2010

VOLUME III JEWS, CHURCH & CIVILIZATION III BIRNBAUM — New Paradigm Matrix — 2010

VOLUME IV JEWS, CHURCH & CIVILIZATION IV BIRNBAUM — New Paradigm Matrix — 2010

VOLUME V JEWS, CHURCH & CIVILIZATION V BIRNBAUM — New Paradigm Matrix — 2010

VOLUME VI JEWS, CHURCH & CIVILIZATION VI BIRNBAUM — New Paradigm Matrix — 2010

VOLUME VII JEWS, CHURCH & CIVILIZATION VII BIRNBAUM — New Paradigm Matrix — 2010

COSMIC WOMB OF POTENTIAL BIRNBAUM — New Paradigm Matrix — 2008

God's 120 Guardian Angels — New Paradigm Matrix — 2009

THE LOST MANUAL I BIRNBAUM — New Paradigm Matrix — 2009

BIRNBAUM ACADEMIC WORKS

4 Summa Metaphysica books (see SummaMetaphysica.com)
1 Summa Supplement book (see Summa-Supplement.com)
2 Crucifixion (see Crucifixion1000.com)
7 JCC   (Jews Church & Civilization) (see Civilization1000.com)
10 MMX books (see MesorahMatrix.com)
3 Summa SpinOffs (see SummaSpinOffs.com)
8 Theory graphics (see TheoryGraphics1000.com)

www.David1000.com

www.SummaMetaphysica.com

NEW PARADIGM MATRIX

New Paradigm Matrix is a multi-media "platform" – based out of Manhattan – which typically publishes works simultaneously in three modalities:

Hardcover for Amazon et al. [see www.AmazonX1000.com]

eBooks [see www.eReader1000.com]

Flip-books online [see www.NewParadigmMatrix.com]

Additionally, the "platform" www.NewParadigmMatrix.com features YouTube videos [see YouTubeX1000.com] relating to symposiums *et al. focused* on the works.

As well, the platform has other contemporary offerings including Birnbaum's Manhattan Observer column
[see www.Observer1000.com]
New Paradigm Matrix endeavors to publish works, which are vibrant and cutting-edge, if not paradigm changers.

David Birnbaum, a graduate of Harvard University, is editor-in-chief of New Paradigm Matrix – as well as the author of several of the works. In addition he is co-editor of the works in the Masorah Matrix division series.

*

Birnbaum's iconic work God and Evil – which intrzoduced his new paradigm Quest for Potential∞ hypothesis, was originally published by KTAV (Jersey City, NJ) in 1988. Four subsequent printings followed in the 1989-2000 period. KTAV still offers the work in its catalogue.

New Paradigm Matrix offers the work as Volume I of 3-volume Summa Metaphysica.

As of October 2020, well over 45,000 volumes

of Summa Metaphysica –

Summa I, II or III – are in circulation globally.

effective January 1, 2021

This New Paradigm Matrix work
is available via multiple modalities:

amazon: www.AmazonX1000.com

online: www.Summa-1.com

www.Summa-2.com

www.Summa-3.com

www.Summa-4.com

contact: NPM1000@yahoo.com

21st CENTURY PUBLISHING
150+ AUTHORS/SCHOLARS

www.Major1000.com

Flip-Books-Academic
PrimePlatforms1000
Crucifixion1000
SummaMetaphysica
MesorahMatrix
Scroll-Downs
Snapshot-Summa-Volumes
UnifyingScienceSpirituality
PotentialismTheory
AcademicBirnbaumImages
ManhattanObserver
TheoryGraphics1000
Civilization1000
HolocaustHijacking
SummaSpinOffs
TheoryOfPotential

SummaCoverage
GodOfPotential

NewParadigmMatrix
BirnbaumAcademicVideos

David1000

Church-Jews
HuffPost1000

BardConference
.com

And what about
  (hitherto iconic)
    Natural Selection / Random Mutation
    aka classic Darwinism ?

And all the King's horses

and all the King's men

Couldn't put Humpty Dumpty

back together again

And the denouement of....

The Former British Empire mob

v.

Outlier Birnbaum's
Potentialism Theory

"All the forces in the world
are not so powerful
as *an idea whose time has come.*"

- Victor Hugo
c.1865, France

WE SHALL SEE

21st CENTURY PUBLISHING

WITH CREDIT TO
KTAV PUBLISHING

www.NewParadigmCatalyst.com

David.Birnbaum.NY@gmail.com

soliciting essays

In due course, we will compile an anthology of essays
500-5,000 words each on Potentialism Theory.

Summa Anthology will be a volume parallel to the one we
crafted for www.Summa-Supplement.com
re: articles published through that point (end of 2015)

You can email me your proposed essay - and I will read and
then forward the piece to the right staffer.
Thanks in-advance.

Let's get you into that anthology.

That way, you will be
'present at creation' ;)

Testimonials also welcome, of course.

David.Birnbaum.NY@gmail.com

note /
Summa-Supplement was an online flip-book only
but
Summa Anthology will also come in a 'regular volume';
not just an online flip-book.

All New Paradigm works are available in multiple modalities, including *gratis - pro bono* via on-line Flip-Books.

See www.AmazonX1000.com to order

[The New Paradigm Matrix Publishing
global network numbers over 2,000,000]

Transform1000.com *

- overlapping -

Major1000.com **

* 25+ Birnbaum academic websites

**35+ Birnbaum academic works

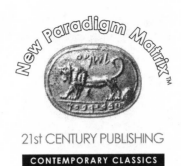

21st CENTURY PUBLISHING

CONTEMPORARY CLASSICS

David Birnbaum
Editor-in-Chief

New Paradigm Matrix
att: David Birnbaum
Tower 49
12 E 49th St.
11th Floor
New York, NY 10017

David.Birnbaum.NY@gmail.com

Morphed Cosmic Order

ISBN 978-0-9801710-5-1
5 1 5 0 0 >

9 780980 171051

Summa Metaphysica series

Summa I - Religious Man: God and Evil (**1988**)

Summa II - Spiritual Man: God and Good (**2005**)

Summa III - Secular Man:
      The Transcendent Dynamic (**2014**)

Summa IV - Quantum Man:
      Morphed Cosmic Order (**2020**)

Made in the USA
Columbia, SC
30 December 2021